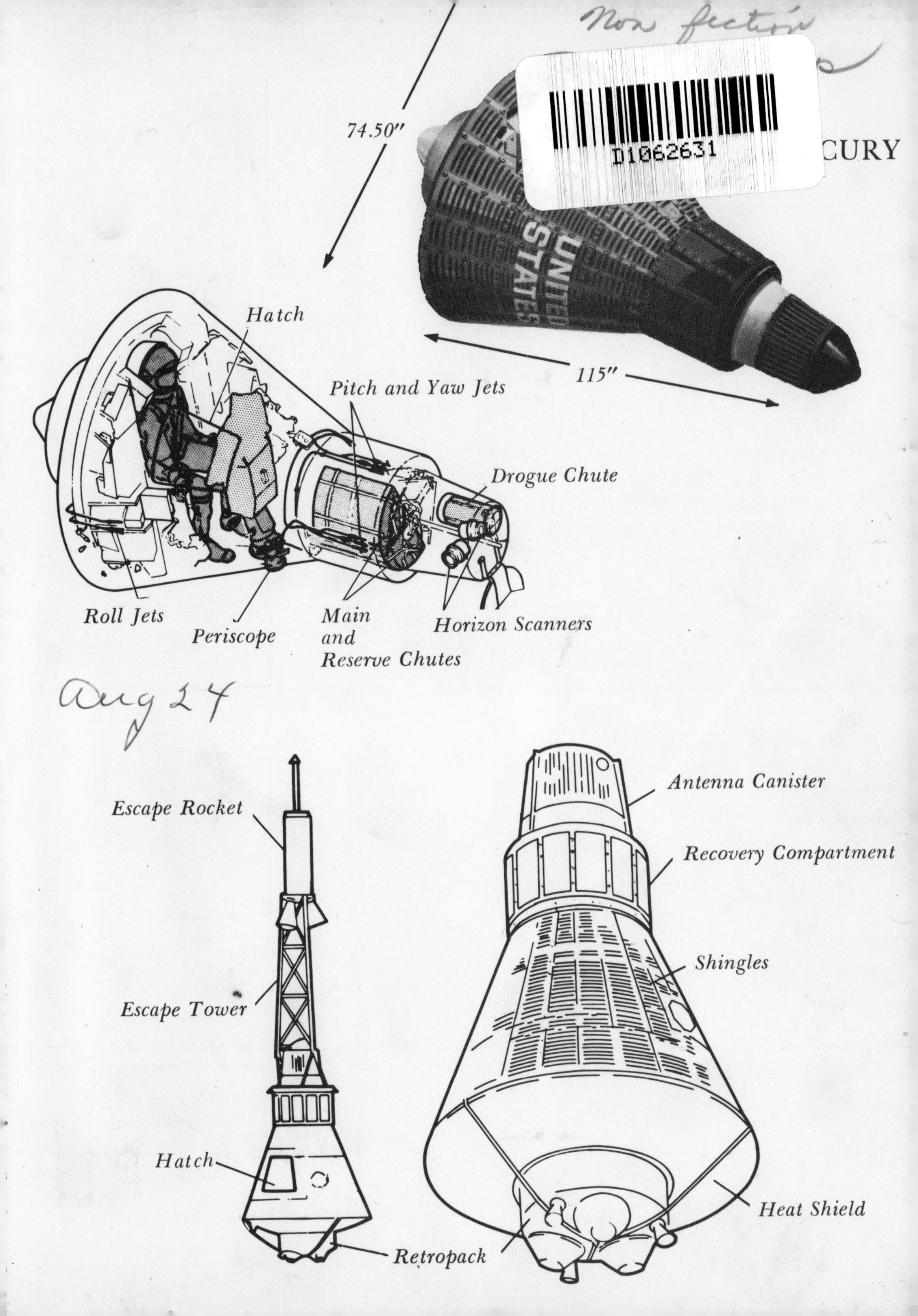
74.50″
CURY
115″
Hatch
Pitch and Yaw Jets
Drogue Chute
Roll Jets
Periscope
Main
and
Reserve Chutes
Horizon Scanners
Escape Rocket
Escape Tower
Hatch
Retropack
Antenna Canister
Recovery Compartment
Shingles
Heat Shield

The first rendezvous in space, December 15, 1965

AMERICANS IN SPACE

FIVE YEARS OF MANNED SPACE TRAVEL

BY
ROSS
OLNEY

NELSON
Camden, N.J.

The author wishes
to thank the following
for their assistance . . .

Henry Still, Northrop Ventura
Charles A. Anezis, Hamilton Standard
Wiley Kennedy, North American Aviation
Ben H. Scarpero, Northrop Norair
M. R. Fowler, Douglas Aircraft
Steve Kerekes, Grumman Aircraft
Maggie Smith, Lockheed-California
Gerald C. Feldman, David Clark Co.
Robert D. Howard, Litton Systems
Edward J. Regan, McDonnell Aircraft
David B. Alter, North American Space
and Information Systems Division
and especially,
Charles Coler, NASA Manned Spacecraft Center,
Houston, Texas, the second most exciting place
in the world.

Published in Camden, New Jersey, by Thomas Nelson & Sons and simultaneously in Toronto, Canada, by Thomas Nelson & Sons (Canada) Limited.

Design by Harold Leach

Library of Congress Catalog Card No. 66-14432

Manufactured in the United States of America

CONTENTS

1

Near dawn on the morning of May 5, 1961, four mournful blasts of a deep-throated foghorn drifted through the mist across a spit of sand in Florida which even then was famous, and which has since become the most exciting place in the world. The sad blasts, dying eventually in the half-light, announced the start of the final countdown for the blast-off of a rocket.

The sounds informed tense onlookers that last-minute safety procedures were in effect, and that the rocket had checked out perfectly and would, indeed, be sent into space.

This was Cape Canaveral, where rocket "shots" were almost routine. But this shot was far from routine. It would be strikingly different from the many others which had been fired in the past.

Several hours earlier, a courageous United States Navy Officer, Alan B. Shepard, had been awakened from a peaceful sleep. Only one other time during the night had he awakened, and then he had quietly walked to the window of his room at the Cape. Looking up into the night sky, he saw thousands of stars. Weather at the Cape was excellent. He returned to bed, and to sleep.

Then, at one o'clock in the morning, he was again awakened. He showered, shaved, enjoyed breakfast with some good friends, then reported for a medical examination. Oddly, neither his pulse nor his blood pressure was unusually high.

Oddly? Yes, for his next step was to be assisted into a silver space suit and then driven, by van, to the launching pad. All America, and much of the world, would ride with him in spirit as he was strapped into a tiny capsule at the nose of the huge, waiting Redstone rocket.

Then he would be blasted into space.

Alan Shepard was one of the men chosen as America's first "astronauts," a word taken from Greek meaning "sailors of space."

Also announced at a press meeting of the National Aeronautics and Space Administration (NASA) on April 9, 1959, were six others:

M. Scott Carpenter: Born on May 1, 1925, he was raised in Boulder, Colorado, and entered the space program after serving as an officer in the United States Navy;

L. Gordon Cooper: A United States Air Force officer, he was born June 3, 1927, and his home town was Shawnee, Oklahoma;

John H. Glenn, Jr.: From Cambridge, Ohio, this United States Marine officer was born July 18, 1921. He was the oldest of the original astronauts;

Virgil I. "Gus" Grissom: Born April 3, 1926, Grissom was from Mitchell, Indiana, and left the United States Air Force to enter the NASA program;

Walter M. Schirra, Jr.: From Hackensack, New Jersey, he was born on March 12, 1923, and joined NASA from the United States Navy;

Donald K. "Deke" Slayton: The only civilian in the original seven, and destined to become Chief Astronaut, he was born in Sparta, Wisconsin, on January 3, 1924.

Shepard, the silver-clad flyer arriving at the launching pad, was born in East Derry, New Hampshire, on November 18, 1923. He had been selected to be the first man in space.

As the white van arrived, tension on the launching pad became almost unbearable. Never in history had an American allowed himself to be strapped into the nose of a bullet, and then fired away at a tremendous speed. Only one man seemed calm in the face of what was to come—Shepard himself. Quietly confident about the outcome of his mission, he joked with fellow astronaut Grissom, who would follow the progress of the rocket from the ground-control station.

Shepard had been amused by a popular recording of the day about astronauts and their particular qualifications and fears. In a Spanish accent (like the recording) he first spoke of the qualities of a good astronaut. He mentioned courage, emotional stability, perfect vision, and low blood pressure.

Then he added, "And you got to have *four legs.*"

"Why four legs?" fired back Grissom, who was playing straight man to comedian Shepard.

"They really wanted to send a dog," Shepard answered, grinning from his white space helmet, "but they thought that would be too cruel."

Then both men doubled over in laughter.

What manner of men can joke among themselves in the face of such a great, and terribly dangerous, adventure?

The original seven were only a handful of several hundred men, almost all test pilots in some branch of service, when the word of "Project Mercury" filtered out. Project Mercury, to put a man in space. Certain original requirements were set.

Obviously the men selected would have to be daring and courageous. Space, with its plunging meteorites, its radiation, and its other unknown dangers, was a completely hostile environment, and the craft to be flown through it was as yet unproven. Such a flight could easily cost a man his life since so little was really known about space, and spacemen, and rockets.

But perhaps even more important than daring, the men selected would need to be the type who remained completely calm under the greatest possible stresses. Unexpected emergencies were sure to appear suddenly (as they did), and these men would be required to react instantly and exactly.

Physical strength was important. Space flight, scientists knew, would be strenuous work.

It boiled down to nerves of steel, muscles of steel, and emotions so well controlled that the man would instantly do the right thing regardless of the crisis he faced in this unknown void of space.

One Air Force General summed it up in a few words.

"What we're looking for," he said, "is a group of ordinary supermen."

Specific qualifications and limits were set. The top age for the new spacemen would be forty. At this age doctors felt that a man had reached his physical and mental prime, and that he still had good years ahead of him after the long training period which would be necessary. Since then, the maximum age limit has been reduced to thirty-five.

Maximum height, with the space capsule size already fixed on the drawing boards, was set at five feet, eleven inches. The capsule was to be seventy-four inches wide at the base, so a man in space suit, helmet, and boots could not be taller than seventy-one inches to begin with or he simply wouldn't fit. Many well-qualified six-footers were disappointed.

Weight, a major factor in over-all payload to be lifted, was also critical. This was set at a maximum of 180 pounds.

No applicant would be considered who had not earned either a formal degree in engineering, or its equivalent. NASA felt that a group of engineers, with their varied opinions and ideas, would help the program immensely.

Only current test pilots, accustomed to modern supersonic aircraft, would be considered. These men, NASA felt, were the type who made split-second decisions as a part of their everyday job, and who remained calm under abnormal stresses.

Personnel cards were fed through computers, and turned up the names of 508 young test pilots who met the basic requirements of height, weight, education, and current status. This number was reduced to 110 after close study and interviews with commanding officers and others who worked with the subjects. After additional tests, including discussions with flying instructors and other co-workers, the number was pared to only 69. This final group of men was called to Washington. They were told only that they would leave their jobs temporarily and that they should report to NASA.

Here, for the first time, they were told of Project Mercury

and America's man-in-space program. Participation would be voluntary. They would leave their own branch of service and join NASA. Thirty-seven officers, after hearing the plan, expressed their gratitude at being considered for such a challenging program, but decided they were not willing to make such a radical change in their careers. They returned to their test-flying jobs.

Thirty-two pilots volunteered.

A series of exhaustive tests started. Although they were already acknowledged to be in near-perfect physical shape (they would never have been called if they had not been), they were subjected to terribly rigorous physical examinations. They were baked at high temperatures, then required to plunge their feet into ice water. They were whirled on giant centrifuges to determine their ability to withstand great pressures. They were required to tackle the "idiot box," an instrument with a whole panel of lights and switches and buttons and levers. Everything that could go wrong with an aircraft, according to one prospective astronaut, was put on this panel. Each function was then thrown out of kilter, and buzzers buzzed and lights flashed and switches flipped. Each man was timed to see how quickly he could restore things to order under the increasing pressure of time and lights flashing and noise screaming in his ears. Panic removed one man from the program.

Each candidate was placed in an absolutely dark room for periods up to 48 hours to test his ability to withstand isolation. In the room was a bed (to be used only during sleeping periods which were pre-arranged), food, a comfortable chair, and a toilet. That was all. Men who found methods of using this isolation time to some advantage, working out mathematical formulas or composing poetry, were considered ideal for the isolation they might later face in space.

All astronaut-candidates were subjected to pressure and lack of pressure in chambers.

They were brought face to face with a battery of psychiatrists who threw questions at them on what seemed like an endless variety of subjects, personal and general. They were probed and punched and needle-pricked and analyzed.

Eighteen remained after this ordeal.

Seven were selected, the very top cream of America's best test pilots. At the introductory press conference, a reporter asked which of them was ready, on that very day, to fly into space. All seven promptly raised their hands.

Alan B. Shepard, one of the seven, walked to the base of the Redstone rocket in his silver space suit. In his hand he carried a portable air-conditioning unit which was attached by hose to the sealed suit. Pausing for a moment, he stared up the length of the 85-foot missile which would carry him into space. Atop the tall vehicle was his tiny capsule, and above this the "escape tower," a framework with small rockets attached which would blast him away from the main rocket in case of trouble during launch.

Although the sky was still dark, bright searchlight beams cut back and forth and arc lights glared, lighting the area vividly. Along beaches nearby, and on the Cape itself, people gathered in greater and greater numbers as launch time approached.

Shepard admired the "bird" (the name spacemen have given their rockets) for a moment, then he stepped into the elevator in the service tower next to the rocket. At exactly 5:20 A.M. he disconnected the hose to his portable air conditioner, slipped off the protective galoshes which had covered his space boots, and squeezed through the capsule hatch. Lying on his back in a form-fitting fiber glass couch, he watched quietly as technicians completed the final hookups. He stifled a chuckle in that most serious moment as, turning to the instrument panel, he saw a sign pasted there by another of the astronauts to help relieve any tension.

NO HANDBALL PLAYING IN THIS AREA

No danger of that, of course, in the tiny little space capsule, cramped with man and instrumentation.

At 6:10 A.M. the hatch was bolted on from the outside and Shepard was alone.

Other astronauts were not idle in the meantime. Deke Slayton, John Glenn, and Gus Grissom were at communications consoles in the control room on the ground. Wally Schirra and Scott Carpenter were crawling into F-106 jet planes to follow the flight of the rocket for as long as they could. Gordon Cooper stood by at a weather station for any last-minute changes that might affect the flight.

Tension mounted. Two days earlier Shepard had endured the same thing, only to have the mission "scrubbed" (cancelled) at the last moment due to inclement weather.

Now he waited . . . and waited, alone atop the powerful rocket. At 6:27 the mournful horns sounded. Everything was ready. The "gantry," or service tower, moved away and the slim rocket stood alone with its human cargo in the nose. Then a "cherry picker" crane, with a ramp at the upper end, moved into position nearby. The ramp was set to lower directly to the hatch as another last-second escape route.

Four nerve-wracking "holds" followed as Shepard waited. Holds are pauses in the countdown for pre-arranged checking or unexpected difficulties with the equipment or weather. During these holds, the countdown stops; then, when the hold is over, the count proceeds toward zero and launch.

The first hold came at 7:14 A.M., over an hour after Shepard had entered the capsule, and only fifteen minutes from launch (T minus 15). Small clouds had drifted over the Cape and threatened to obscure the clear sky necessary for a rocket shot. The count was set back thirty minutes as technicians hoped for a clearing sky.

During this delay, however, a small inverter near the top of the Redstone started to overheat. This is a critical device which supplies alternating current to the instruments in the capsule from the direct current provided by the batteries. Eighty-six minutes later, the inverter was repaired and ready.

Meanwhile Shepard, alone in the capsule at the top of the rocket, waited.

Twenty-one minutes later the count again stopped. This time

technicians wanted to recheck a computer which would help predict the trajectory of the rocket and its impact point in the downrange recovery area.

Finally, at T minus two minutes and forty seconds, the last hold occurred. Scientists became worried about the pressure on the liquid oxygen fuel in the Redstone. Gauges disagreed on the exact pressure. If this could not be corrected, and specific measurements made to determine the precise pressure, the mission could not be rescheduled for another 48 hours. Liquid oxygen fuel (LOX) is both highly volatile and corrosive, and cannot be left in missile tanks. It must be removed, the tanks scrubbed and cleaned, and then put back in just before the next scheduling. This procedure takes two days. Fortunately, the problem was solved by bleeding off some of the fuel and the final countdown resumed at 9:23 A.M.

Shepard had been strapped into the capsule for over four hours, and still he did not show worry, tension, or excess excitement.

He was as comfortable as doctors and scientists could make him, under the circumstances. His form-fitting couch was designed for him alone, for his own body shape with its particular lumps and curves and angles. It would not have worked for any other man. His pressure suit, a man-made balloon, was tailor-made for him also. The suit fit the man so snugly that thirteen zippers were required to seal him into it. Completely air-cooled, the suit even contained tiny barometric sensors which indicated to the astronaut any changes in pressure. Closing the visor after such a warning of a drop in cabin pressure would activate a device which automatically inflated the suit to proper pressure. The space suit is, according to one astronaut, a cabin-within-a-cabin.

A constantly refreshed supply of oxygen is automatically provided for the astronaut. Suit temperature can be set according to the desire of the man inside. Shepard preferred his own suit's inside temperature to be a cool 60 degrees, but some of the other astronauts wanted a warmer 72 degrees inside their suits.

If the oxygen should fail inside the suit, a back-up system

automatically activates, and if this should fail a third system is available.

At 9:34 A.M. the countdown reached zero.

Flames belched from the lower end of the Redstone and it shuddered on the pad. For an instant the missile hesitated, then slowly, too slowly it appeared to onlookers, it began to climb away from the pad. In spite of appearances, everything was going according to plan, or at least going according to what scientists *thought* was going to happen the first time they rocketed a man into space.

Shepard's voice crackled through headsets on the ground as the rocket picked up speed.

"Roger, lift-off and the clock is started," he drawled without a trace of worry in his steady voice. His reference to the "clock" was to the time-to-retro-fire clock aboard the capsule. It would tell him exactly when the retro-rockets should fire and bring him back down.

"This is Freedom Seven," he called, using the name he had given the capsule in honor of America, and in honor of the seven astronauts. "The fuel is 'Go.' One-point-two G. Cabin at fourteen psi. Oxygen is 'Go.' "

"Go" is a space term meaning everything is functioning normally. Calmly, as the rocket thundered up through the atmosphere shaking the ground far below, the astronaut was relaying vital information.

Deke Slayton, the ground communicator, broke in.

"You're on your way, Jose," he said with a grin in his voice. This, again, referred to the recording that Shepard had found so amusing.

Alan Shepard had no real idea what might happen next. Scientists and engineers on the ground had no real idea. Certainly plans, critically careful plans, had been made. Everything that might possibly have anything to do with the flight and its outcome had been minutely studied. Shepard himself had been subjected to nearly identical stresses and strains of the rocket ride, on the ground beforehand. Everything which could be taken into consideration had been taken into consideration.

Still, when a man does something which no other man has ever done before, and he does it in a very dangerous element with hundreds of unknowns involved, he lays his life on the line. Shepard's life was on the line.

If everything went well, a great deal would be learned to prepare the next man for his ride, and the next and the next. Doctors and scientists on the ground had to know every feeling, every emotion of the man in the capsule as the flight progressed. Shepard quickly started his complicated and busy schedule of actions and reports. Meanwhile, every physical function of the astronaut was being monitored on the ground by doctors. Medical sensors attached to Shepard's body relayed all vital information about heart beat, blood pressure, and other details.

At one minute after launch the capsule started a severe vibration, but it had been expected. Shepard was passing through from sonic to supersonic speed and then through a zone of maximum dynamic pressures as the forces of air density and speed combined at their peak.

The astronaut waited calmly through the turbulence, then reported, "It's smoother now . . . a lot smoother."

Slayton acknowledged from the ground.

The Redstone streaked further into dark space, faster and faster. At two minutes after launch it had climbed twenty-two miles and was moving at an amazing 3200 miles per hour, faster than man had ever traveled before.

"All systems 'Go,' " reported Shepard.

Everything was normal.

Rocket engine cutoff occurred on schedule, at two minutes and twenty-two seconds after launch. Instantly the escape tower blasted free and streaked away from the nose of the capsule. It would no longer be needed, and had been programmed to rocket away after the flight was underway. It would fall back towards Earth and burn to a cinder in the thicker air below.

Then, again according to plan, the capsule disengaged from the booster. This was an extremely critical maneuver, and one which could not be duplicated for practice on the ground.

Suppose it didn't break away smoothly? Or suppose its sudden breakaway threw the capsule unit into uncontrolled spinning or tumbling? These things did not happen, but were only two of the unpleasant possibilities facing this first American in space.

Alone in his little space capsule, detached from all earthly ties, Alan B. Shepard became weightless, the first American spaceman to do so. Here, traveling at an astounding *5000 miles per hour,* he could place an object in the air before him . . . and see it remain there, unmoving. In fact, another astronaut on a later flight watched a tiny washer float up into view in his capsule, while a third chuckled over droplets of orange juice hanging suspended before him in a weightless state.

A space capsule, free from its booster, has three separate and distinct motions: pitch, roll, and yaw. One of Shepard's jobs was to see if the control system designed for space flight actually worked in space. It had on the ground, of course, but space is quite different. Tiny jets of hydrogen peroxide would squirt out from various nozzles placed strategically around the capsule, depending upon the way the control stick was moved. These jets, according to scientists, would push the capsule into different directions in its weightless state.

According to Shepard in the book *We Seven,* a story of the astronauts: "I switched over to the manual control stick, and tried out the pitch, yaw, and roll axes in that order. Each time I moved the stick, the little jets of hydrogen peroxide rushed through the nozzles on the outside of the capsule and pushed it or twisted it the way I wanted it to go. When the nozzles were on full blast, I could hear them spurting away over the background noise in my headset. I found out that I could easily use the pitch axis to raise or lower the blunt end of the capsule."

(The automatic control system had turned the capsule around so that it was actually flying backwards, ready for reentry.)

"This movement," Shepard goes on, "was very smooth and precise, just as it had been on our ALFA trainer (a ground simulator). I fed the yaw axis, and this maneuver worked too. I could make the capsule twist slightly from left to right and back again, just as I wanted it to. Finally I took over control of the roll motion and I was flying Freedom Seven on my own. This was a big moment for me, for it proved that our control system was sound and that it worked under real space-flight conditions."

Another of the high points of Shepard's flight into space came soon after. His flight plan called for him to extend his periscope and look below. His spontaneous exclamation snapped over the radio.

"What a *beautiful* sight!!"

From his vantage point in space, 115 miles high and south of Florida, he could see up the coast of the United States to where clouds obscured Cape Hatteras. Across Florida to the west he could see Tampa Bay and as far northwest as Pensacola. He could see Andros Island and Bimini. He could see hundreds of miles in all directions.

He was witnessing a sight never before seen by man.

But suddenly, too soon it seemed, he was informed by ground communicator Deke Slayton that it was time for the retro-fire maneuver. This is the firing of the three small rockets on the broad heat shield to his rear which would slow the capsule just enough to allow gravity to pull it downward to its recovery area.

Five minutes and fourteen seconds after launch the first retrograde rocket fired, exactly on schedule. Five seconds later the next one fired, and five seconds later the third fired. Shepard felt his tremendous speed reduce slightly.

He was on his way down for a searing flight through the Earth's atmosphere which would heat the blunt end of the capsule to a blistering 1000 degrees temperature because of the friction of the air rubbing against the speeding capsule. On schedule the retro-package containing the rockets fell away from the heat shield, the job of the little rockets completed. Shepard watched the package drift away and downward.

Perhaps the most critical phase of the flight, or of any space flight, is the reentry phase. Meteorites and other bits of matter fall into the Earth's atmosphere by the millions every day, from specks the size of dust to much larger particles. We are not aware of these because they burn up as they fall deeper and deeper into our layer of air, though we are many times aware of the "shooting stars" they appear to be at night. They burn for the same reason the capsule would burn, because of the terrible heat from the friction of air rubbing against them as they fall.

A space capsule is nothing more than a man-made meteorite falling back into thicker air . . . and the same thing, total disintegration due to heat, could easily happen to it. Scientists foresaw this possibility and designed the space capsule to withstand the heat, not by making it heavy and thick (actually the sides are quite thin), but by forming it a certain way and then attaching the heat shield on its wide, blunt end.

So long as the blunt end is forward, the ceramic heat shield takes the full brunt of the heat and dissipates it by actually burning away. The thickness of the shield, and the speed at which it burns, is carefully calculated so the shield will last until the heat phase of the reentry is over.

If the automatic control system fails to position the capsule with its heat shield forward, or if the pilot is unable to position it in this way in the event of an automatic control failure, the result would be tragic. Everything, including the astronaut, would burn to nothingness as the capsule, appearing to be a shooting star, disintegrates.

Even properly positioned, a capsule at night would leave a trail of fire as the shield burns away. Many astronauts have commented on the "fireball" aspect of their capsule as it reenters the atmospere.

During Shepard's first flight into space, this was just another of the many unknowns he faced with cool courage. Calculations said the heat shield would work. Tests proved it would work. It burned away at just the right speed, and dispelled the terrible heat perfectly. In every test the capsule came through in fine shape.

But these tests were conducted on, or controlled from, Earth. No astronaut had risked being burned to death in case something failed.

Now Shepard was preparing to undergo just that risk. He was about to find out if the theories were correct. Would the heat shield work in space, with a man behind it? And would the capsule hold its position so that the shield could do its job properly?

With infinite care, Shepard positioned the capsule at exactly a 40 degree down angle, with the heat shield forward. This was where all calculations said it should be. Then, typical of the cool daring of these men, he returned to other experiments, knowing that he could do no more. The shield would either work, or it wouldn't.

He felt the pressure of the air slowing the capsule, pushing him into his seat as it pushed against the blunt end. Finally a force of eleven G's, eleven times the force of gravity on Earth (causing him to weigh eleven times his own weight) was exerted against his body.

But he was ready for this force. On centrifuges all of the astronauts had endured much more, to the point where they were unable to speak normally and had to grunt out single words with great effort.

As his altimeter spun through mile after mile of descent, Shepard called "OK, OK, OK," to ground controllers, who were listening tensely. He wanted them to know he was well, or the exact point at which he encountered trouble. Outside, the heat shield glowed red hot and started to melt away. Through this period the capsule went through a planned gentle roll in a counterclockwise direction, spinning at about ten degrees per second. This was to even out the heat, and the burning of the heat shield. Outside the temperature climbed to a searing 1230 degrees, but inside all was well. Never did the inside capsule temperature climb to over 100 degrees, and Shepard was comfortable in his space suit at a mild 82 degrees.

G forces began to reduce at 80,000 feet and by the time the capsule had fallen to 30,000 feet all seemed well. Falling at 300 miles per hour, the "drogue chute," designed to position the capsule for the main-chute ejection and to stop any oscillation, deployed as it was programmed to do. Through his periscope Shepard could see the little parachute far above. At 15,000 feet a ventilation tube opened automatically to draw cool, fresh air into the capsule. At exactly 10,000 feet the main parachute deployed automatically, along with recovery radio antennas.

Shepard uttered a brief message to the hundreds of technicians, engineers and scientists waiting at communications centers.

"All OK."

These people who had a direct part in the flight of Freedom Seven were not the only ones waiting with bated breath for the final "splashdown." Crowds gathered around public television sets across the nation, in Grand Central Station in New York, on Michigan Avenue in Chicago, and in several locations in Los Angeles, and in nearly every home in America TV sets were tuned in on the historic space flight. Countless millions were watching tensely.

American space scientists had been confident. They had planned carefully and methodically, without rush, and they were certain that nothing would go wrong. They were sure of America's space technology, and so they had allowed this whole first effort to be televised to the public across the world, as it was happening.

If anything went wrong, this country's prestige, in view of the impressive space efforts of the Soviet Union, would have suffered greatly. On April 12, the Soviet Cosmonaut Yuri Gagarin had orbited in *Vostok I,* a feat widely acclaimed throughout the world. Other peoples would have seen our mistake in the glare of worldwide publicity. But if things went well, our confidence in our Mercury program couldn't be mistaken.

Things *were* going well. Alan Shepard floated slowly toward the surface of the Atlantic Ocean 300 miles south of Cape Canaveral. At 1000 feet altitude he looked down through the capsule periscope and saw the surface coming up. He braced himself, later commenting that the landing jolt was very similar to that received by a Navy pilot as he is launched from the catapult of a ship. Noticeable, but mild.

As the spacecraft hit the water he hit the switch which would kick loose the reserve parachute in the upper end. This would lighten the capsule at the top and reduce the oscillation of the unit so that it would float upright in the water around the capsule, another item to help ships and airplanes find it quickly. Meanwhile, automatic broadcasts were going out from direction finding gear aboard the spacecraft. Shepard checked the capsule for leaks and, finding none, sent a message the world had been awaiting.

He was down, and he was safe and well. The mission had been a complete success. Americans cheered.

Overhead a helicopter had arrived on the scene and was preparing to recover the courageous astronaut. Shepard heard the hook from the hovering aircraft catch into a hook at the top of the capsule. Then the pilot called.

"You have two minutes to come out," he joked by radio.

Shepard answered, "I'll be out in 30 seconds."

He opened the hatch and crawled into a sling suspended from the aircraft directly overhead. A tumultuous welcome was awaiting him on the recovery ship, at the Cape, and across America. At the White House he would receive a medal from President John F. Kennedy.

This young Naval officer had proven, at the risk of his life, that space travel was possible. Certainly this had been only a very hesitant beginning to an adventure that would carry men far into space, into week-long orbits, to the moon, and beyond, but he had blazed the trail.

He proved how lucky we are to be living in this age. Thanks to him and the others who made his flight possible, man will soon walk upon the moon! And so as our parents and grandparents spoke of Lewis and Clark, Fremont, and Zebulon M. Pike, all great explorers, we will speak of Alan B. Shepard.

But the adventure had just barely started.

2

Alan Shepard's capsule had carried him 302 miles downrange in fifteen minutes and took him to an altitude of 117 miles. His maximum speed had been 5,036 miles per hour.

The doctor's report immediately after the flight stated, "Subject felt calm and self-possessed. Some degree of excitement and exhilaration noted. He was unusually cheerful and expressed delight that his performance during the flight had actually been better than he had expected. He was more concerned about performing efficiently than about external dangers."

During his flight he lost three pounds . . . a fast, but very hazardous reducing program.

This had not been a random effort by unprepared people. For months, even years, previous to the flight in space, experiments had been in progress. Some were successful, some were not. Most of the failures were heartbreaking. Occasionally they were humorous.

The Mercury-program launch phase started with MR-1 (Mercury-Redstone One) on November 21, 1960, after numerous other missile launches. As far back as 1957 a launch had been attempted, but Vanguard TV-3 failed. In 1958 seventeen launches were attempted; seven succeeded, ten failed. By 1959 the record was improving. Of nineteen launches of unmanned rockets, eleven satellites were injected into orbit. Only eight failed to achieve orbit.

Then, in 1960, sixteen orbits were achieved and thirteen attempts failed. One of the outstanding failures, humorous but educational, was that first MR-1. This was man's first attempt to launch a Mercury capsule which would eventually carry an astronaut. To understand the funny failure, we must first understand the amazing Mercury capsule.

This little space cabin has a mind of its own, and is one of

First Seven—The original seven astronauts chosen for the Mercury program are shown in pressure suits. Left to right, are (front row) Walter M. Schirra Jr., Donald K. Slayton, John H. Glenn, Jr., and M. Scott Carpenter; (back row) Alan B. Shepard, Jr., Virgil I. Grissom, and L. Gordon Cooper, Jr.

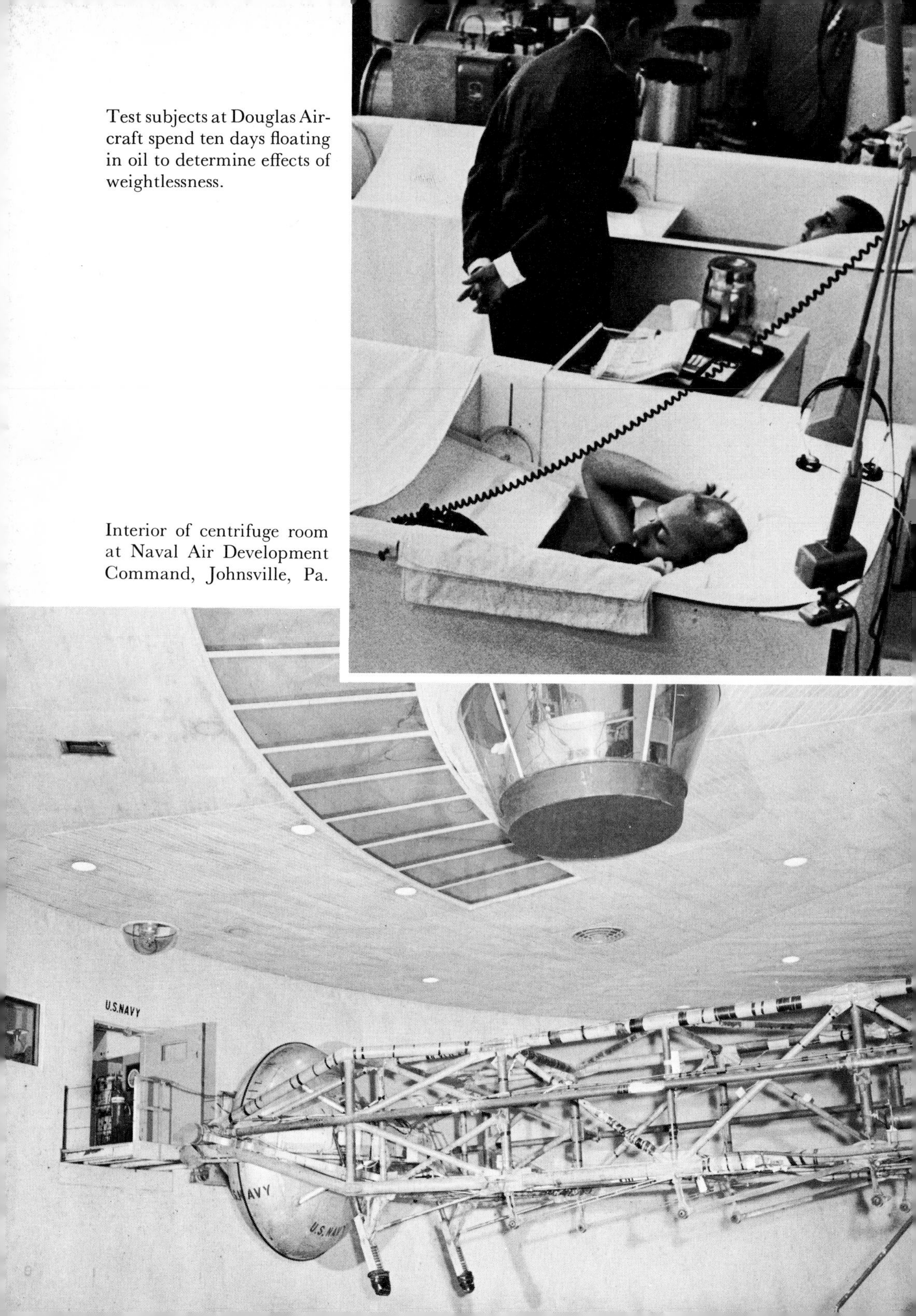

Test subjects at Douglas Aircraft spend ten days floating in oil to determine effects of weightlessness.

Interior of centrifuge room at Naval Air Development Command, Johnsville, Pa.

In California is a man-rated space chamber which can duplicate conditions found in outer space.

Here a portable life-support system is going through tests in a chamber which simulates vacuum conditions in space.

Mercury Liftoff—Mercury-Redstone Three (Freedom Seven) was the first manned space flight of this program and was a ballistic flight carrying Astronaut Alan B. Shepard, Jr. The test objectives were to familiarize man with brief but complete flight experience including liftoff, powered flight, weightless flight (for a period of about five minutes), reentry and landing phases.

Alan B. Shepard, Jr., suiting up during preflight activities at Cape Canaveral, Florida.

the most complicated, sophisticated pieces of equipment known to man. In it are thousands and thousands of extremely delicate parts, each absolutely precise, and all wired together with over *seven miles* of wiring.

Miniaturization was the order, since the "back-up" system was used throughout the capsule even though size and weight were critically important. Consider the problem of the engineers. A rocket, the Redstone, was available to lift the capsule into space. But the Redstone, already built and fixed in size- and weight-carrying capacity, could not be substantially altered. So the space cabin had to be built to fit the rocket. And the two units had to mate perfectly.

Then, inside the space cabin itself, all systems had to be backed up with duplicate systems in case of the failure of a primary system. Communications, life-support, capsule control, everything had to be duplicated. Finally, the entire complex of systems would have to operate automatically in case an astronaut became disabled or unable to perform in space.

When a new airplane is built it takes years of hard work from drawing board to flight test, yet engineers have all the previous years of knowledge to draw upon. They already know and understand powered flight in the atmosphere. They have the findings of the Wright brothers and all other knowledge from that point on at their fingertips when they design a new supersonic fighter or bomber or transport.

But here was an entirely new type of craft. This one would be flown in *space,* and no research material was available. No spaceship had ever been built before. The entire craft had to be designed and built from scratch, and be produced quickly. The task seemed impossible.

They didn't even know what *shape* to make it. Should it have wings? Perhaps it should be shaped like a ball. These forms were seriously considered, and models were tested, then the forms were rejected. A shape similar to a bell was finally selected.

The job of constructing this complicated machine, with the help of the brilliant astronauts who were to fly it, was completed. The Mercury spacecraft was born.

As many systems as possible were included. In some cases, a certain system had to be rejected in favor of a more important one. Television, for example. Some engineers wanted a camera in the capsule on the very first mission, but size and weight restrictions finally made the inclusion of this system impossible. But each system in the capsule did have a back-up system, which had been the plan. Each system was both manual and automatic. Some systems, such as the life-support unit, actually had two back-up systems besides the primary one. This craft could, according to plan, support a man in space where he would instantly die of suffocation or of some unknown hazard without its protection.

Yes, and the small cabin was given a mind of its own. Not only could it be controlled by the astronaut, and by the ground, but it could also control itself if other controls failed. If the life-support system, for example, should begin to fail, built-in warning systems would inform on this failure. Then, if something wasn't immediately done about it, the capsule would take corrective actions all by itself. If the capsule feels itself falling through the Earth's atmosphere, it considers its own altitude and, at the proper moment, releases its own parachutes. If, during launch, the capsule senses a problem in the rocket below, it merely blasts itself away from the trouble, carrying the astronaut with it. The little cabin even informs the astronaut by blinking a warning light at him immediately prior to this drastic action.

"Brace yourself, pilot," the light seems to say.

And they roar away. Then, rather than crashing, the capsule releases parachutes which lower it gently to the ground or ocean. All this happens before a man could even begin to consider the original problem which caused it.

But this brainpower could make for problems . . . and did in the one case in question.

Examine, for example, the test firing of MR-1 before Alan Shepard's first flight in space. In the newspapers you read merely that it had failed and that another test firing was scheduled. Scientists are still chuckling over what really happened.

It was a tense moment at the launch complex. For the first time a full-scale Mercury-Redstone launch was to be attempted. Here the rocket, and the capsule which would eventually carry an astronaut, had been attached together and set up on the pad. Everything seemed ready for the firing as astronauts and other scientific personnel stood by during the final countdown. On the pad several hundred yards away one of the weirdest performances in the history of space flight was about to take place.

But through it all capsule, rocket, and other systems performed perfectly . . . just as they had been "trained" to do.

In order, this is what happened. The countdown reached "zero" and smoke and flame shot from beneath the tall Redstone. Thunder rolled across the pad. The booster moved upward slowly and ponderously until it reached a grand altitude of *one inch.* At that altitude, the engines suddenly stopped and the rocket settled back on the pad, swaying precariously for a moment.

The capsule, far above at the very nose of the rocket, then came alive. In an instant, the escape tower blasted away in a rush of flame, arcing beautifully out over the Cape but leaving the capsule still attached to the panting rocket.

That didn't end the display. Engineers in the blockhouse stared in stunned silence as the performance continued out on the pad.

Following the blast-off of the tower, a parachute popped from the nose of the capsule, then another popped out, and they sagged down over the sides of the capsule and booster like great limp rags.

Smoke and debris littered the area.

Then silence settled once again. There sat the Redstone, puffing out white clouds of LOX (liquid oxygen) as though it were waiting for a launch, and perched far above, the capsule sat serenely, its flashing beacon light signaling the completion of its mission through the billowing folds of the parachutes. Silently, radio beacons beamed directional messages to help the recovery forces downrange pinpoint the exact location of "splashdown."

A total failure? Not at all.

NASA engineers, after minutely studying and finally deducing the cause of the chain of fireworks, were quite pleased. Two power plugs mounted at the base of the Redstone were supposed to pull free at exactly the same instant.

When NASA scientists say "exactly," that is just what they mean.

Overlooked, however, had been the fact that the prongs on one power plug were one-eighth of an inch shorter than the prongs on the other. Instead of pulling free together at blast-off, as they normally should have done, the plugs disengaged one at a time, with the shorter one pulling free first.

The lag between the two, to give an idea of the exactness of space science, was only *twenty milliseconds.* Divide one second into one million parts, then take twenty of these parts, and you have an idea of the interval between the pull-out of the plugs.

But this interval was all that was necessary to flash warnings through the booster and capsule systems and to cause the resulting display.

A new circuit was thrown in automatically, this one telling the abort-sensing mechanism in the Redstone to shut down the rocket engines instantly. This is precisely what it should have done, and exactly what the Redstone did.

At that point the capsule (with a mind of its own) reacted exactly as it was supposed to do. Its brain realized that the Redstone's engines had shut down, in response to the signal it was *supposed* to receive at an altitude of thirty-five miles. So it blasted away the escape tower as being no longer needed.

The mission, as far as the capsule was concerned, was sailing along smoothly in space. So, as it was supposed to do, it started to tick off the "return-from-space" sequence of events, and then it quickly noted an alarming fact. Tiny barometric pressure gauges inside the capsule sensed that the spacecraft was at a dangerously low altitude—which indeed it was—and so the capsule fired out the parachutes which would lower it to the ocean. The light beacon, intended to attract searchers, obediently turned on, and radio messages from the capsule started.

These recovery aids worked so well that two Navy P2V aircraft, stationed downrange in the recovery area to assist in the pickup, quickly turned about and started to "home in" on the launching pad.

The capsule had only omitted one step, and it had a reason for that. It did not disengage from the booster, as it would have done before the "descent" sequence started. However, it was still at one G surface pressure, while its brain knew that it should be pulling .05 G at the time of separation. So it stood fast, and did not disengage.

The cause of the failure was corrected, and two months later MR-1 was re-launched with complete success. Forty-eight minutes after launch, the first spacecraft designed to carry a man was picked from the ocean by the aircraft carrier *Valley Forge.* This occurred in January of 1961. To be doubly sure before a human astronaut attempted the ride, MR-2 was fired on January 31, 1961. The passenger, dressed in a silver space suit cut down to his own size and with all accessories also scaled down, was Ham the chimpanzee. He came through the ballistic flight in fine shape.

Meanwhile, launch of MA-1 (Mercury-Atlas One) had been attempted, and had failed. This would be the capsule and booster which would carry an astronaut into orbit. Starting in 1960, the MA program progressed through an orbital ride by Enos, another space-chimpanzee, in MA-5.

Tension at the Cape, however, was building as July 21, 1961, approached. America had done it once, and on that date we were to try another suborbital ballistic flight with an astronaut in the capsule.

As calm and ready as the first one had been, this astronaut was awakened at 1:10 A.M., served breakfast at 1:25, and subjected to a last-minute physical examination at 1:55 on a cool Florida morning at the Cape. Far out on the pad, the Redstone with its capsule waited.

At 3:58 a.m., Virgil I. "Gus" Grissom crawled into the space cabin, named Liberty Bell Seven. He was to wait there three hours and twenty-two minutes before his great adventure started.

Three holds later, Grissom heard the voice of Deke Slayton conclude the long countdown.

". . . five . . . four . . . three . . . two . . . one . . . ignition!"

Then, almost immediately, he heard, "Lift-off!"

He heard something else, too. Coming through from another transmitter was the voice of Al Shepard, who had made the exciting ride himself. Again referring to the recording "The Astronaut" by Bill Dana, Shepard, with a Spanish accent, drawled, "Don't cry too much . . ."

The comic astronaut had been asked what he planned to do during his long ride in space. He had answered with mock seriousness, "I plan to cry a lot."

The lift-off of MR-4, with Grissom at the controls, was smooth and precise, and the unit rocketed away into space.

The ballistic ride was as perfect for Grissom as it had been for Shepard, with only the recovery offering a problem. He flew the capsule, and he noted the ground and water far below. He reported on the total blackness of space and he reported on the strange sensation, bordering on fear, of watching a shaft of pure sunlight inch its way across his torso from lower left. The brilliant beam of light, in the total blackness of the capsule, finally disappeared as the capsule completed its turnaround.

Grissom fired his retrograde rockets manually, exactly on schedule, describing the feeling as a "kick in the pants" when the rockets suddenly slowed his motion through space. He watched the dead package fall away, and he listened to the curious roar inside the capsule as it bored its way through the blistering air outside.

He felt the mild shock of the parachutes as they opened far above him to lower him into the ocean, and he noted the "bump" as the capsule hit the water. Once again, with amazing precision, helicopters were on the scene immediately.

Then Gus Grissom's trouble started. It may have been as some wags at the Cape suggested, that the capsule was very well named Liberty Bell Seven, but a symbolic crack should never have been painted up the side of the bell-shaped spacecraft. For the explosive hatch blew off prematurely.

Grissom had armed the hatch and prepared it for firing. Then his plan was to wait until a helicopter had lifted the capsule a few feet so that water would not enter when he fired off the hatch. Fortunately, as things worked out, he had disengaged himself from most of the connections inside the capsule in preparation for leaving it, and fortunately the astronauts had insisted on a "water dam" rubber collar at the neck of their suits to prevent water from filling the suit. Certainly the rubber collar is uncomfortable, but in an emergency (such as what was about to occur) the collar could be a lifesaver.

Another omission, though, nearly cost Grissom his life.

Before the capsule could be lifted, the hatch blew off with a great thud and water rushed into the cramped spacecraft. There was no panic, though there was some quick movement. Calmly, but rapidly, as he had been trained to do in an emergency, Grissom disengaged himself from the remaining connections inside the capsule then crawled through the hatch, fighting the inrush of water.

Meanwhile, the recovery helicopter overhead, noting what had happened, quickly dropped its hook and engaged the ring at the top of the capsule. Grissom floated off a few yards, watching. Still there was no great problem.

Then things began to get complicated.

A "glitch," a space term meaning the same as the World War Two "gremlin" which caused unexplainable malfunctions on aircraft, had blown off the hatch, and trouble was mounting. Grissom's suit began to fill with water through an air-conditioning port he had forgotten to close in the rush of getting through the hatch. The helicopter pilot overhead was unaware of this new danger and from his position he could not see that the astronaut was sinking deeper and deeper into the water. The pilot continued to struggle with the sinking space capsule, assuming that Grissom was in fine shape in his protective space suit.

But the capsule was getting heavier and heavier as the water rushed in. Helicopter engines strained and red warning lights flashed on across the helicopter instrument panel.

It was no use. The capsule had become too heavy to lift and in fact so heavy that it was dragging the struggling helicopter down toward the surface. The pilot released the hook, and the capsule sank into the ocean far too deep for recovery.

Grissom, by this time, was nearly under himself. At the last possible moment, he was lifted from the water and wet, discouraged (at the loss of his capsule), and bedraggled, he was flown to the recovery aircraft carrier. Only his helmet, which had been found after it floated free of the sinking capsule, was saved.

The helmet, according to the Navy officer who returned it, was found floating near a ten-foot, man-eating shark.

Even though his capsule had been lost, Grissom's flight was another success, and another great step towards one of America's most exciting journeys into space. His telemetry systems had functioned perfectly, relaying valuable information back to earth. He himself was able to answer detailed questions about the flight, adding greatly to man's knowledge about space flying.

The reason for the premature firing of the explosive hatch was never determined—but that's how "glitches" are. They happen, and are never explained. To our great fortune, we had a perfectly trained specialist present who was quickly able to over-

Recovery of Mercury-Redstone Three (Freedom Seven) Astronaut Alan B. Shepard.

Mercury-Redstone Four (Liberty Bell Seven) Astronaut Gus Grissom.

Project Mercury Astronaut John H. Glenn, Jr., enters the Friendship Seven spacecraft during the last part of the countdown on February 20, 1962. At 9:47 a.m., the Atlas launch vehicle lifted the spacecraft into orbit for a three-orbit mission, the nation's first manned orbital flight.

Liftoff of Mercury-Atlas Six (Friendship Seven) with Astronaut John Glenn aboard.

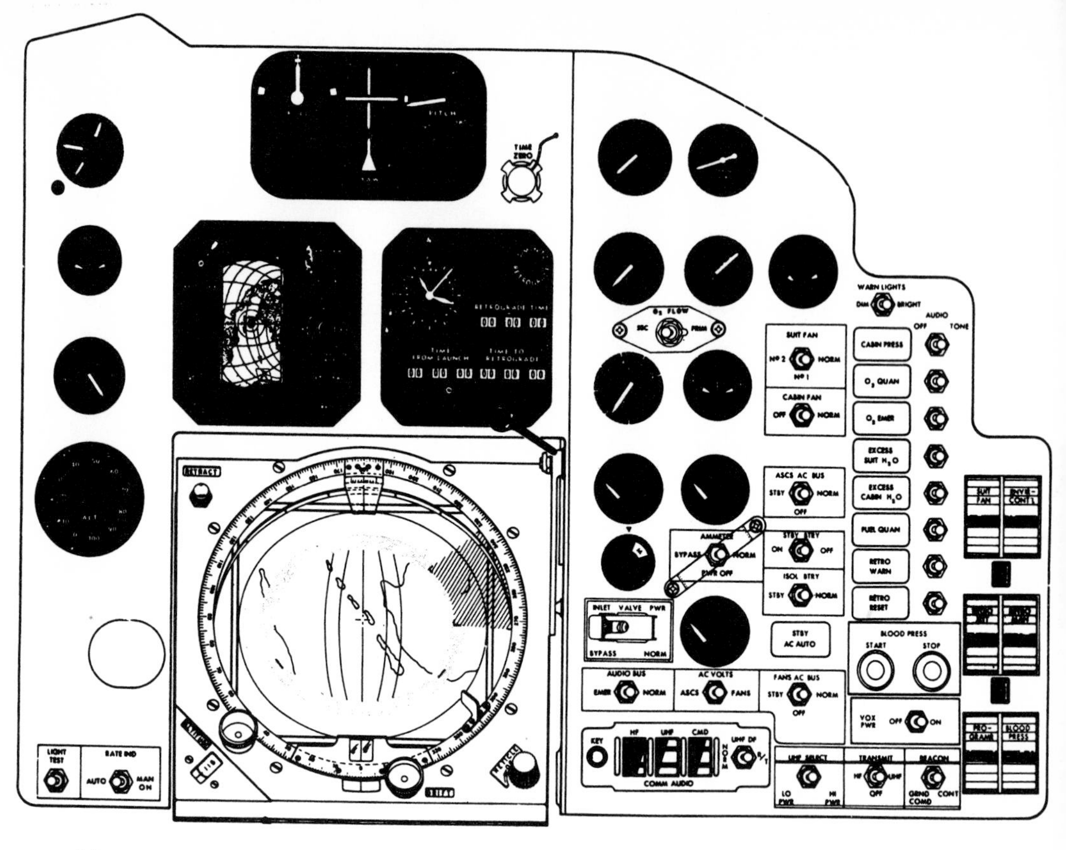

Mercury spacecraft instrument panel.

Drawings show how heat shield drops down to form "landing bag" after reentry through atmosphere. This recalls John Glenn's problem with the loose heat-shield indication on the ground.

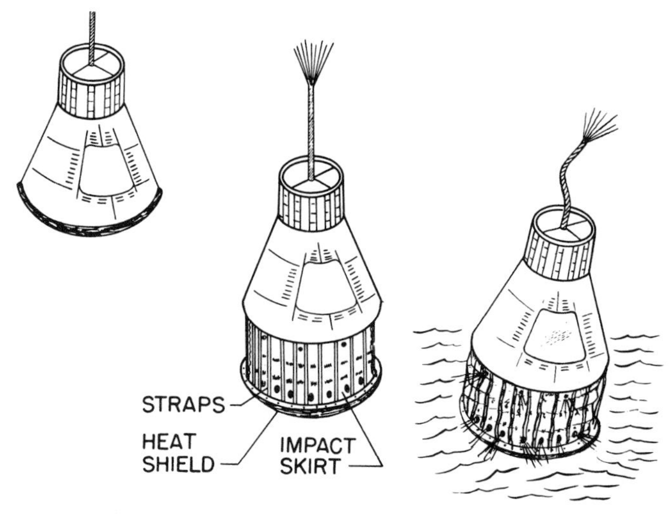

come this misfortune and turn a potential tragedy into a fine success . . . and to further prepare the Cape for the morning of February 20, 1962.

Two men had undergone suborbital ballistic flights, and had proven the capability of the Mercury capsule. The time had come to test it under the most dangerous possible conditions—the conditions of *orbital* flight.

There is a confusion as to just exactly why a heavy object "floats" around the world in orbit. Some feel that the moon's gravity "cancels" the earth's gravity and an object merely floats. Others feel that the object is whirled by some giant centrifugal force. Still others feel that the object "blasts" its way through space, holding itself in orbit by sheer power.

Certainly all of these things have a bearing on the subject, but none is precisely correct.

To be perfectly accurate, an object in orbit is actually *falling* at every moment of its stay. To come home, it merely falls a little *slower,* to start the long plunge. Picture this if you can.

You are standing on a perfectly smooth Earth; that is, no mountains anywhere. The surface of the Earth is completely flat for as far as you can see in all directions, and on from there. Now take a high-powered rifle, and fire it horizontally. Let's follow the bullet. As it travels away at an extremely high rate of speed, several things can happen. Assuming it was fired perfectly level, it will either eventually draw away from the surface of the Earth as the Earth curves away and downward beyond the horizon (remember, we have fired it with great power so that it will travel on and on) or, with somewhat less power, it will eventually fall to the ground at some great distance away from us.

The third possibility is "orbit." If the bullet were fired with *exactly* the right speed and power, it would *fall* as the Earth *curves away and downward.* With gravity, and the Earth's curvature, the bullet would continue to fall around the curve of the Earth. Now if this were done in the heavy atmosphere of the surface of the

Earth, this atmosphere would quickly slow the bullet or (at the tremendous speed necessary for orbit) burn the bullet up. Then, too, we do have mountains and cities and other things which would stop the bullet.

So we fire the bullet high above Earth, into an almost total lack of atmosphere and far above anything which might stop it.

As the "bullet" (the capsule and booster) rockets into space, it turns until it is "injected" into a *horizontal* orbit. You've seen this turn if you have watched our space shots on television or in person. The final push, before rocket cutoff, is horizontal. The final, precise speed, altitude, and location are the "keyhole in space" rocketeers are seeking. If the speed is *precisely* correct (within a few miles per hour of the thousands of miles per hour required) and the altitude, and the attitude and location are all *exact,* the capsule and its booster will *fall* into orbit. With no atmosphere to slow it or change its direction, it will continue to fall down around the curve of the Earth.

Retrograde rockets, mounted on the capsule, are finally fired *into* the line of travel, *slowing* the capsule slightly and causing it to drop back to the ground . . . just as our bullet would do if it were by some means slowed down.

This, with a man aboard, is what technicians at the Cape hoped to accomplish.

John Glenn, Jr., was the astronaut selected to pilot this most ambitious flight. As he prepared himself with long hours of study and physical conditioning, the booster and the Mercury capsule were being readied. Fortunately, John Glenn was not a superstitious man, for the capsule being prepared for his history-making flight was the thirteenth such capsule built by the McDonnell company in St. Louis, Missouri.

Glenn named his capsule Friendship Seven, again in honor of the original seven astronauts. The flight was planned for three orbits of the world.

The new Atlas booster was checked and re-checked. The Redstone had done its job well, but for this orbital flight more power was needed so the three-engined Atlas had been chosen. During the initial part of the lift-off, all three engines would be firing, the sustainer engine and both outboard engines. Then the two outboard engines would cut off after two minutes and the sustainer engine would finish the job of injecting the capsule into orbit. Finally the whole booster assembly would drop away, and Glenn would be alone in orbit in his capsule.

At least everybody hoped it would work out this way.

A world-wide communications network was set up under the direction of astronaut Alan Shepard. This would be necessary for the first time since our astronaut would be ranging around the world, yet immediate communications with him at every moment would be vitally necessary. Over 140,000 miles of wire were used in this network for primary and back-up communications equipment, teletype and data transmitters.

The net ran from the Cape to Bermuda, to the Atlantic Ocean ship *Rose Knot,* to the Canary Islands, to the Indian Ocean ship *Coastal Sentry*, to Muchea, and then to Woomera in Australia. From there it went on to Canton Island in the Pacific Ocean, to Kauai Island in Hawaii, to Point Arguello in California (or to Guaymas in Mexico as an alternate in this critical retro-fire zone), to White Sands in New Mexico, to Corpus Christi in Texas, to Eglin Air Force Base in Florida and back to the Cape. At no point during its around-the-world flight, providing everything worked as planned, would the capsule be lost from radar sight or radio sound.

Primary and secondary recovery areas were arranged, and ships and planes were stationed in these areas. The primary area was in the South Atlantic, not too many miles from the Cape where the flight would begin.

But delays occurred. In an operation of this type, nothing can be left to chance. Everything must be as perfect as man can make it. John Glenn waited with a stoic calm during these extended delays, continuing his exercises and practicing on mission simulators so that he would be in peak condition when the time came. America waited with increasing impatience, but with the confident knowledge that when the flight went, it would go in the best possible shape.

John Glenn's mail built up by the day with letters from around the world, from people who admired and respected his calm courage and who wanted to wish him well on his dangerous mission.

Most of them, in any case.

Every man in the public's eye gets "crank" letters, and even John Glenn received a few. One lady insisted that the delays were God's way of telling Glenn that he should not be tampering with the Heavens. Another letter, this one from a man, insisted that Glenn had an undiscovered gall bladder problem. The man insisted that he could diagnose this ailment from a cover photo of Glenn he had seen on a magazine.

One young boy touched John Glenn with a valentine (this day was drawing near). He said on the card, "I have *space* in my heart for you."

Glenn tries to answer every letter (most of the astronauts do, in fact) but he is still working on the stack which never stopped growing, even after he left the NASA program.

Gradually, one by one, the problems with MA-6 were tackled and solved. The date was set. It would be February 20, 1962.

At last, the morning arrived.

A break in the heavy cloud cover over the Cape was promised by the weathermen, so the involved countdown continued. Glenn, in the company of astronaut Deke Slayton (who was scheduled for the next orbital mission), Dr. Bill Douglas, the astronauts' physician, and others, rode in the white van to the launching pad. He waited in the van through two holds in the countdown, then after a final weather check confirmed the previous forecast, he left the van and stepped to the elevator in the gantry tower beside the Atlas. Everybody stopped his work for this last glimpse of the astronaut, and crews smiled and waved their good wishes for a safe return.

These technicians, whose names will never become famous, had worked killing hours to prepare the capsule and booster, and to iron out the problems. Their "moment of truth" had come along with the astronaut's.

Glenn paused, smiled and waved back, then the elevator whisked him to the capsule level. Scott Carpenter, one of Glenn's best friends and his back-up pilot, was there to shake hands and wish him well, and to help him squeeze into the capsule.

Even this is a most critical maneuver and is done very carefully. A torn suit or a damaged instrument could delay the flight for hours. Glenn entered the capsule without incident.

This is a precarious and perhaps fearful place for an astronaut to wait. He is alone and the gantry has been moved away. He is on his back 75 feet in the air at the top of a thin rocket. Before him is the greatest, most dangerous flight in his life. Waiting there he can feel the motion as the rocket sways slightly in the wind. In fact he can cause this motion by shifting his body, for the rocket is held there in its rigid state by very little. The very fuel in its tanks is partially responsible. The booster could crumple and collapse without this fuel, so thin are its walls and so heavy the load it carries.

The astronaut reclines in his form-fitting couch directly atop some of the most highly inflammable fuels known to man. A wrong spark, a static charge, and . . . ? Astronauts busy themselves with other matters, pushing such thoughts from their minds.

Through two more holds Glenn waited and finally the countdown neared zero. The automatic engine-starter sequence kicked in, and that was the point of no return. From that point on, only the abort-sensing mechanism could stop the blast-off, and that would cause Glenn's capsule to be ripped from the Atlas and blasted out over the water.

As the engine-starter sequence activated, the voice of Scott Carpenter broke in with fervent seriousness.

"Godspeed, John Glenn," the astronaut radioed to his good friend.

They would meet again, these two friends, and spontaneously embrace each other in a warm greeting after an even more hazardous mission in the near future.

The voice of Alan Shepard intoned the final few seconds of the countdown, and the three mighty engines ignited. Across America, citizens held their breath. This is a highly critical phase of a flight in space. An astronaut can thunder away from Earth in triumph if all goes well, or he can be cremated alive in boiling flames if a serious failure should occur.

All went well.

U.S. space scientists once again proved that careful, extremely methodical study and planning is the key to success in space. They could speed things up, they knew, and get to the moon quicker, but at the certain cost of lives. As it is, we must even now face a tragic, but absolute, statistic. The laws of chance and odds . . . which are seldom wrong . . . tell us by careful calculation that we will lose two astronauts in our struggle into space to the moon. Let us hope that this time the odds are wrong, even though we know these men are attempting fantastically dangerous missions.

For three seconds the giant Atlas stood fast on the pad, then as the engines built up enough thrust, the huge holding clamps at the base dropped away and the rocket lifted. Slowly at first, then with increasing, doubling and re-doubling speed, it roared away from the Cape. During its lift-off, it would develop an astounding 360,000 pounds of thrust.

"The clock is operating," called Glenn. "We're underway."

According to astronaut Glenn, there were four major hurdles to clear on his way into orbit. The first was the launch and the roll program to head him into the proper orbit. The second critical area was that portion of the flight where the vehicle, and the astronaut, pass through the highest aerodynamic forces. This occurred about forty-five seconds after launch, at an altitude of about 35,000 feet. Here severe buffeting and vibration shook the spacecraft and booster.

The third hurdle, a most critical one also, is the phase of the flight where the two outboard engines shut down and fall away. This also progressed smoothly and Glenn was outside the Earth's atmosphere.

At two minutes and thirty-four seconds after launch the escape tower jettisoned and Glenn watched it streak away at high speed, pulled by the little rocket motors which might have pulled him and his capsule away from the booster had trouble developed on the ground. The unit disappeared quickly.

Only the sustainer engine was powering the flight, and this was being controlled from the ground to guide the vehicle through the critical "keyhole" in space. Finally, at five minutes and one and four-tenths seconds after lift-off, the sustainer engine shut down. The bolts which held the booster and capsule together exploded and the two units separated. The capsule turned slowly so that its blunt end was forward. This is the position in which the first orbital flight was made, as were the first suborbital flights.

In case of trouble, the capsule would be in position for an instant reentry.

The insertion had been perfect, and the fourth major obstacle cleared. The first American spaceman was floating weightless *in orbit.*

Looking out his window, Glenn exclaimed, "Oh! That view is *tremendous*!"

He could see for hundreds of miles in all directions. Nearby he could see the Atlas booster drifting along by itself. It was about 200 yards away, eventually drifting out of sight along its own non-critical orbit.

The word came from Al Shepard on the ground. Computers had been digesting all information on the flight to that point.

"You have a 'Go' for at least *seven* orbits," he called.

Glenn was jubilant. The mission had been planned for only three orbits, and only three would be flown, but the insertion had been perfect enough for seven, and probably seventy, if food and enough fuel had been aboard.

Working closely with the ground controllers, Glenn first established his retro-fire times exactly. Then he started checking his attitude-control systems, automatic, manual, and fly-by-wire (a system utilizing both the previous ones, and proven extremely important later).

Riding backwards in the capsule in orbit, according to astronaut Glenn, compared to riding backwards in a jet airliner at about 30,000 feet. Leaving the Atlantic Ocean to begin his drift across the dark continent of Africa, Glenn saw his Atlas booster for the last time. Eventually it would fall and burn to a cinder in the atmosphere, meanwhile becoming only a "space object" with a specific number assigned so that it would not unduly clutter radar sets tracking other missions.

It wasn't long before Glenn encountered a problem which would need solution on future orbital missions. He was having difficulty storing small items of equipment in the weightlessness of space. Here on Earth, when we put something down we merely set it down and leave it. In space this is not possible. A camera, for example, may just float around inside the capsule, drifting into the way of other experiments or, worse, bouncing around until it damages delicate equipment.

Glenn took several such small items along, including cameras, rolls of film, filters, binoculars, photometers, and an odd instrument for making astronomic and physical measurements outside the capsule called an extinctionspectrophotopoleriscopeocculaogravogyronkynetometer.

Space flight is indeed complicated. Most people couldn't even say the word, let alone use the equipment.

However, as many complicated words are shortened, this was also shortened to "Vaos Meter" in honor of Dr. Vaos, the man who invented it. The storage problem, though, with this and the other instruments, remained throughout the mission.

Glenn witnessed his first sunset over the Indian Ocean, noting that the sun was a perfectly round disc and with a clear, intense bluish-white light. He watched the black shadow of sunset move across the Earth far below, and he watched the myriad colors as the sun dropped out of sight. He looked down at the Earth, and in hushed tones called it a "black pit" of total darkness.

Then he saw a sign of man in the black pit from the loneliness of space. The citizens of Perth, Australia, in a salute to the brave man passing over in his capsule far above, had turned on every light in the city. Street lamps, neon signs, car lights, house lights, stadium lights, even flashlights, gleamed up from the darkness. Glenn radioed his thanks for the patch of visible brightness on the black Earth. At about that time, from the Australian station, he received another bit of good news. His insertion speed had been predicted at 25,730 feet per second. His actual speed had been 25,738 feet per second, an astounding eight feet per second difference. The launching's near-perfection had been confirmed by computers.

Then, suddenly, it was sunrise. In only an hour and thirteen minutes, Glenn had progressed from daylight through sunset to darkness, and back to sunrise again . . . and to one of the strangest sights of his mission.

All around him, for as far as he could see, were thousands and thousands of tiny, luminous particles. For a moment he thought he had drifted upside down and was looking at a new field of stars, but that wasn't it.

In the book *We Seven* Glenn repeats his radio message to the ground.

"This is Friendship Seven. I'll try to describe what I'm in here. I am in a big mass of very small particles that are brilliantly lit up like they're luminescent. I never saw anything like it. They're coming by the capsule, and they look like little stars. A whole shower of them coming by. They swirl around the capsule and go in front of the window and they're all brilliantly lighted. They probably average seven or eight feet apart, but I can see them all down below me also.

He was asked if he could hear or feel any impact with the capsule.

"Negative," he reported. "They're very slow; they're not going away from me more than maybe three or four miles per hour. They're going at the same speed I am approximately. They're only very slightly under my speed. They do have a different motion, though, from me because they swirl around the capsule and then depart back the way I am looking."

As sunrise advanced, the surprising particles disappeared.

They have never been completely explained. Other astronauts have seen them, notably Scott Carpenter, but exactly what they are is unknown. Probably specks of dust and paint from the capsule itself, though Glenn is not at all sure of this. Perhaps they were tiny snowflakes formed by condensation of water vapor from the control nozzles of the capsule, or maybe they were a layer of tiny needles sent up by the Air Force in a previous space experiment and encountered by accident.

They were not imaginary, though one psychiatrist later joked with John Glenn, asking, "What did they *say,* John?"

The specks, however, faded in importance with chilling suddenness. As it headed into its second orbit, the capsule relayed a message to Earth unknown to John Glenn. The message lowered a pall of fear and uncertainty over the mission-control center.

The heat shield, according to the telemetry data, had worked loose. It was, in fact, designed to come loose after its job was finished, and then function as an impact bag when the capsule hit the ocean. But to come loose *before* it had completed its primary job spelled *tragedy.*

Technicians huddled in the control center. One ray of hope presented itself, assuming the telemetry data were correct. Heavy metal straps held the retro-rocket package to the face of the heat shield, and to the capsule itself. The retro sequence included cutting away these straps and allowing the retro package to fall away after the capsule had been slowed down. But suppose the metal straps were the only thing left holding the heat shield in position on the blunt end of the capsule.

It was quite possible, and even probable.

On the other hand, the signal from the capsule might have been wrong in the first place. The heat shield might still be firmly in place between astronaut Glenn and the soon-to-follow blazing reentry.

A capsule had never reentered with the retro package remaining in place after use, but it was possible that cutting it away as planned might also allow the critically important heat shield to drop away. Mercury control decided not to worry the astronaut, but at the same time to question him about the heat shield indication they had received.

Glenn's first clue of something amiss came with a message from the Indian Ocean CapCom ship.

"We have a message from Mercury control for you to keep your landing-bag switch in OFF position, landing-bag switch in OFF position, over."

"Roger," answered Glenn, wondering to himself why the landing-bag switch had suddenly assumed an importance halfway through the flight.

Moments later, as he passed over Australia, he heard the voice of astronaut Gordon Cooper.

"Will you confirm the landing-bag switch is in the OFF position, over?" asked Cooper.

"That is affirmative," replied Glenn, by then realizing a serious problem may have been indicated on the ground. He also knew that the problem could have to do with the life-saving heat shield. The "landing-bag switch" allowed the shield to drop down a few inches, exposing a leather skirt with holes in it. This skirt, around the whole base of the capsule, was designed to momentarily trap air as the capsule hit the ocean, cushioning the impact. If the landing-bag switch had flashed "ON" in the mission-control center, it could mean that the heat shield was already loose. With nothing to hold it in position, it was sure to slide about during reentry, allowing the leather to quickly burn away . . . and then it would fall completely off the capsule.

Astronauts are not excitable, nor do they spend a great deal of time worrying about situations which might be, or which could happen. Even in the face of great danger, they calmly analyze any situation they must face. In this case, Glenn said nothing. He put his faith in the highly trained men on the ground, knowing that there was little he could do at that moment or they would have instructed him to do it.

"You haven't heard any banging noises or anything of this type at higher rates?" asked Cooper.

"Negative," answered Glenn in an even voice.

The mission progressed smoothly, with frequent requests from the ground for information concerning the landing bag. Through the second orbit, Glenn worked in the capsule, putting thoughts of the heat shield from his mind. He took photographs of the Earth far below and conducted other experiments in the weightlessness of space.

At one point he corrected his time-to-retro-fire clock, which indicated an error of one second. Retro-rockets were due to fire four hours, thirty-two minutes and thirty-eight seconds after launch. One second of error could mean many miles of difference in the recovery area in the ocean below. One second in space could mean the difference between immediate pick-up and hours of waiting in a bobbing, tossing capsule in the ocean. The truth of this would show up later, in another orbital flight, when Americans waited agonizing hours for the recovery of another astronaut.

But Glenn's clock was corrected, and everything appeared normal. Everything but the heat shield, perhaps the most important piece of equipment on the capsule.

"We'll see you in Grand Turk," Gus Grissom radioed, his voice full of confidence.

"Yes, sir," Glenn fired back.

Grand Turk Island was the first landfall of the astronauts after their ocean pick-up.

Typical of the calm humor of the men in the space program, Glenn called down to Earth.

"This is Friendship Seven. In forty-five seconds I would like to have you send a message for me, please. I want you to send a message to the commandant, U.S. Marine Corps, Washington. Tell him that I have my four hours required flight time in for the month and request flight chit (flight pay voucher) be established for me."

Pilots in the service are required to fly four hours minimum each month in order to qualify for flight pay . . . but this was the first time a man met the requirement by flying four hours in *space.*

Meanwhile, technicians on the ground studied the heat-shield problem. Different procedures were considered, then rejected. If the heat shield had worked loose, the worst possible thing had happened, but suppose the signal indicating that it had worked loose was wrong? Then actions to counteract this condition could be disastrous. Although it had never been done before, controllers decided to go ahead with the reentry with the retrograde rocket package *remaining in place,* after the rockets had been fired. If this caused the capsule to whirl out of control, it would not be as bad, potentially, as having the heat shield drop away when the retro package dropped away.

Glenn was informed of the exact nature of the problem, and the proposed solution. He did not argue with, nor even comment on, this life-or-death decision. If he had other possible solutions in mind, he remained silent and once again put his faith and confidence in the trained men on the ground.

The reentry sequence started.

At the same time, due to a malfunction in the control system, Glenn was "flying by wire," controlling the attitude of his capsule manually. A mistake here could also mean that the capsule might turn into a "shooting star," if it were permitted to drift into the wrong attitude with respect to its penetration of the atmosphere.

At this point, Glenn's heartbeat increased to 96 beats per minute, only 10 points higher than normal, and another tribute to the calm way in which he was facing this potentially deadly hazard.

Falling through the atmosphere, he waited for the searing heat to eat through the capsule walls (in case the heat shield dropped away) and into his body. It would be quick, he knew. Meanwhile, he made minute movements of the "swizzle stick," the control stick, to hold the capsule in the right position.

Suddenly he felt a violent thump at his back, on the heat shield.

Was the shield dropping away? Would he, in an instant, feel the heat burning through?

Through his window he saw the metal straps holding the retro package fall away in flames. A bright orange glow built up around the spacecraft.

His steady voice intoned the message, "A real fireball outside." He continued to control the capsule in its downward plunge.

Then, on the ground, transmission ceased. John Glenn's voice could no longer be heard from space. Worried technicians waited, praying.

Seconds, according to one scientist, "passed like days on the calendar."

Al Shepard continued his calls to the capsule.

"Friendship Seven, this is Cape, do you read?"

No answer.

"Seven, this is Cape, please answer, over."

Silence from space.

Unknown to ground controllers, a layer of ionization had built up around the reentering capsule, cutting off all radio communications. Radar still had the falling spacecraft in "sight" but was it a sleek capsule, or a burned out chunk of metal? Now, technicians expect this temporary "blackout." All they knew, as they waited for Friendship Seven, was that at that very moment the capsule was being subjected to a heat pulse temperature of about *9500 degrees,* and that the heat shield itself was about 3000 degrees . . . if it was still in place.

The silence became almost unbearable.

Then suddenly, through strong interference, came the voice from space. ". . . loud and clear . . . how me . . . ?"

Sighs of relief filled the control room. A few men cheered.

Shepard answered quickly. "Roger. Reading you loud and clear. How are you doing?"

"Oh, pretty good," Glenn answered laconically.

The heat shield had functioned properly. The signal received on the ground had been incorrect. All was well with the astronaut.

Glenn watched his drogue chute deploy, then his main chute.

"Ready for impact," he called.

Then, twenty seconds later, "Here we go!"

Ten seconds later, "Friendship Seven, impact! Rescue aids are manual."

He was down safely in the ocean, awaiting pick-up. He watched the approaching destroyer *Noa* through his periscope as it came alongside. The capsule was lifted aboard, Glenn blew the hatch, then he stepped out.

America's first orbiting spaceman had returned to a wild welcome aboard the destroyer, later on the aircraft carrier to which he was transferred, and later yet with the ticker-tape parades in cities across America. President Kennedy called him immediately and later invited him to Washington where Glenn was given a medal for heroism.

On the deck of the destroyer *Noa,* in tribute to John Glenn, two footprints were painted where his space boots first hit as he crawled out of his capsule. They are still there.

The Mercury program was at its halfway point. Three successful launches of men into space, one into orbital flight, was the record thus far. The Gemini program, where America would send *two-man* capsules into space, was in the near future. Already a second team of astronauts was being selected to bolster the number of spacemen available.

John Glenn, America's new hero, returned from Grand Turk Island in triumph. He rode down Pennsylvania Avenue in Washington on his way to a speech before Congress, and over 300,000 people stood in the rain to cheer him and his pretty wife, Annie. Improvised signs, thrust up from the screaming crowds, announced the nation's delight.

"A Marine for the big one! Welcome, John!"

"Apogee, Perigee, rah, rah, rah, Glenn!!"

In suburban Arlington, where Glenn's son attended high school, "Welcome to Dave's Dad."

In a firm voice, Glenn started his speech to the nation's leaders with a modest, "Mr. Speaker, Mr. President, members of the Congress, I am only too aware of the tremendous honor that's being shown us at this joint meeting of Congress today.

"When I think of past meetings that involved heads of state and equally notable persons, I can only say that I am most humble to know that you consider our efforts to be even in the same class."

Seated left to right—L. Gordon Cooper, Jr., Virgil I. Grissom, M. Scott Carpenter, Walter M. Schirra, Jr., John H. Glenn, Jr., Alan B. Shepard, Jr., and Donald K. Slayton, all original Project Mercury flight personnel. Standing left to right—Edward H. White, II, James A. McDevitt, John W. Young, Elliot M. See, Jr., Charles Conrad, Jr., Frank Borman, Nell A. Armstrong, Thomas P. Stafford, and James A. Lovell, Jr., all selected in September, 1962, to join the original seven in the Gemini and Apollo projects.

Astronaut Walter M. Schirra, Jr., and the centrifuge.

Astronaut Walter M. Schirra, Jr., going over his flight plan in Mercury Control Center with Chris Kraft, Flight Director.

Spacecraft Sigma Seven and Atlas booster during simulated flight on pad #19 at Cape Canaveral, Florida.

Actual photos of a manned Mercury Capsule landing in the ocean. This is the successful end of Mercury-Atlas Eight (Sigma Seven) with Wally Schirra aboard. This was called the "bull's-eye" mission because it landed so near the recovery forces.

Aerial views of USS Kearsarge, C.V.S. 33 and escort ships of recovery group which participated in the recovery of Astronaut Walter M. Schirra, Jr., following world orbital flight.

Glenn's use of "us" and "our" and "we" is a tradition of the astronauts. When speaking of the flights they make, they use these terms to indicate that others were involved to make the project a successful one. In fact, they insist that they are only the figurehead in an effort involving thousands of equally important people.

They, the astronauts, are all deeply patriotic. Glenn indicated this as his speech progressed. ". . . pride in our country and its accomplishments is not a thing of the past. I know I still get a real hard-to-define feeling down inside when the flag goes by."

The astronauts have a deep faith, and John Glenn typifies this. Once, long before he was famous, he was making a trip with his family to Washington, D.C., to do some Christmas shopping. On the journey, the parents discussed with their two children, David and Lyn, the meaning of the holiday. Suddenly, Glenn stopped the car in a small town.

"The best way to illustrate the spirit of giving," he said to his children, "is to do something about it."

From a local justice of the peace he got the name of a needy family. Then he took his own family shopping. They filled bags with gifts and food, and delivered them to the family of eight children, whose father was out of work, and whose mother was sick.

Then the two families sang hymns together. The Glenns then continued on their trip.

John Glenn, Jr. Here was a hero, a brave patriot, and yet a devout, modest man, and America took him to her heart. Like the other astronauts, John Glenn found a permanent place in the history of the United States.

But more was to come in Mercury. Soon America would cry, and then laugh with relief.

4

On May 24, 1962, Mercury-Atlas Seven was scheduled. Named Aurora Seven, the flight would be made by Deke Slayton and would be another three-orbit mission.

Slayton, however, endured a disappointment that might have broken an ordinary man. Months of preparation and terribly hard work, training above and beyond the call of duty, and personal sacrifice were his contribution to the planned success of MA-7. He wanted this flight to be the best of all, and he worked and planned for the day he would go into orbit.

Then, at what seemed like the last minute, doctors discovered a minor "heart murmur" in this physically razor-sharp man and, after a great deal of soul searching, scratched him from the mission. For the first time in Mercury history, a back-up pilot would make the flight.

Scott Carpenter felt honestly bad about his friend's disappointment, but deep down his heart surged. Along with Deke, and Wally Schirra and "Gordo" Cooper, he'd waited impatiently for his own chance, and now it appeared to have come.

These men are highly competitive, and Deke Slayton argued and pleaded. He had doctors on his side who agreed that if there was a heart sound, it could not be important. Some doctors said he would perform flawlessly and that any heart problem he had, if he had a problem at all, was so minor it should be ignored.

But it was not ignored, and Carpenter planned for his ride. Slayton, true to the spirit of the Mercury program, pitched in with hard work to make his friend's ride a successful one after he had done his best to keep himself scheduled, and failed.

On that morning in May, everything looked good. The astronaut was in fine shape and ready, the capsule and booster checked out perfectly, and the weather was good. Briefly, a brush fire in the Everglades brought a pall of smoke to the launching pad, but after a 45-minute hold, the launch countdown progressed.

“The launch,” according to Carpenter, “was a snap.”

His mission was to prove the systems that John Glenn had tested, and to learn if they functioned identically in another man’s hands. Also, he would perform experiments in space that Glenn had not had time to do.

The escape tower, according to Carpenter, “took off like a scalded cat,” and he was weightless in space.

At sunrise he saw John Glenn’s “fireflies” and he maneuvered his capsule for a better look. Passing over Australia, he maneuvered the capsule to attempt to see flares which had been placed on the ground to test the visual acuity of the astronaut in space. The first time over the Cape he released a balloon from his capsule, then he maneuvered for a better look as it drifted along tethered behind him.

At that point Carpenter suddenly became aware of, and appalled at, his lack of fuel. The maneuverings called for by his flight plan had drastically depleted the supply. Rather than end the mission, the ground controllers suggested he drift in flight and conserve fuel.

Fuel, to an astronaut preparing to reenter, is of critical importance . . . easily as important as the heat shield itself. Whether he must do it himself, or whether his capsule does it automatically, the attitude of his spacecraft must be held precisely. Fuel is needed to position the craft to this correct attitude in space, and to hold it there, and there is no room for error. If the craft should run out of fuel, it might tumble and burn up.

Americans, watching closely on television, began to hold their breath. So far we had been fortunate. In spite of problems in the unforgiving void of space, no tragedy had occurred. Would this be the first time?

Even then, Carpenter found humor in his near-fuelless, drifting state, He attempted to eat, and found that every time he opened a packet of cookies, supposedly covered with a crumble-proof wax coating, they did crumble anyhow.

“Every time I opened the bag, the crumbs would come crowding out like a swarm of bees, and I tried to pick them out of the air and eat them to keep them out of the cabin atmosphere."

He toyed with his camera, attempting to place it in the air before him in a perfectly motionless state. He did succeed, one time, in getting it to hover there before his eyes for several minutes. Then he would bounce it away with one finger, and catch it in the other hand. Then, like a child in this new and exhilarating state of total weightlessness, he would spin it before him and it would spin on and on with nothing to stop it until he, himself, did.

He had put worries about lack of fuel completely out of his mind. Men on the ground were trained to face emergencies such as fuel depletion. They would make a decision, and he would follow their recommendations. Why worry?

While preparing for reentry, he inadvertently struck the capsule side during a sunrise. Instantly a whole cloud of "fireflies" surrounded the outside of his capsule. Perhaps he had solved the mystery by this move. Scientists agree that it is quite possible the fireflies are specks of dust and paint clinging to the side of the spacecraft, drifting away as the craft is flown, and visible only when the light rays strike them just right.

At reentry Carpenter's fuel supply was critically low, yet he had to position the craft properly. The retro-rockets fired, and he started down. Then, to make matters worse, a tank which had registered 7 per cent fuel remaining was actually found to be empty. The danger magnified, and Americans watched tensely.

Carpenter maneuvered the craft carefully, attempting to hold it in position and still conserve the dwindling fuel for the long, hot plunge downward.

He reported muttering to himself, "This has been the greatest day of your life. You have nobody to blame for being in this spot but yourself. If you do everything correctly from now on, you may make it. If you do not, you just won't."

He disappeared into the communications "blackout" phase of reentry. A suspense writer couldn't have dreamed up a more tension-packed plot. America came to a standstill as the tiny capsule burned down through the atmosphere in the ocean south of Florida.

There it disappeared.

Although rescue and recovery craft rushed to the point of assumed splashdown, they did so with heavyhearted crews. Across America, people cried. Finally, it appeared, after a brilliant record of space triumphs, we had lost an astronaut. Scott Carpenter, a brave pioneer, could not be contacted. Apparently his fuel supply had not lasted through the long, hot plunge, and his craft had strayed from its critical attitude.

Still, mission control called and called, though it was far past time for him to emerge from the communications blackout. Americans waited and watched sadly.

What everybody did not know, until computers reported it, was that Carpenter's capsule had veered to the left at retro-fire, and that the firing had been a long (in space terms) three seconds late.

They did not know that Carpenter, at that very moment, was sitting in his capsule, in the ocean, some 250 miles from the planned point of splashdown. He could hear controllers calling him, but his own equipment was not powerful enough to reach them.

He breathed "Thank you, Lord," fervently, and settled down to wait. His direction-finding equipment, he knew, would pinpoint his location in the ocean eventually.

Carpenter's distraught countrymen waited three tense hours before the word came that he was in fine shape and awaiting pick-up. It was at the pick-up that he and John Glenn embraced each other warmly.

Later this modest man said with deep sincerity, "I would like to apologize for the concern I caused . . . If I had known how concerned you were, I would have been concerned."

In spite of the near-miss, the space effort continued. Carpenter had been given too many things to do in space, too many experiments which had burned up valuable fuel. This mistake would not occur again. And something else was happening to further the effort.

On October 1, 1962, NASA welcomed some newcomers to duty.

Nine new astronauts were introduced to the world. Like the first seven, they were all test pilots, all married, and all ready and eager for a ride in space. The average age was thirty-two and one half, slightly younger than the first group. Spacemen could now be six feet tall, since the capsules were being designed larger. These pilots, along with some of the first seven, would be the Gemini spacemen:

Neil A. Armstrong, born August 5, 1930, from Wapakoneta, Ohio, a civilian.

Frank Borman, born March 14, 1928, from Gary, Indiana, a U.S. Air Force pilot.

Charles Conrad, Jr., born June 2, 1930, from Philadelphia, Pennsylvania, a U.S. Navy pilot.

James A. Lovell, Jr., born March 25, 1928, from Cleveland, Ohio, a U.S. Navy pilot.

Elliot M. See, Jr., born July 23, 1927, from Dallas, Texas, a civilian. (Died in plane crash, February 28, 1966.)

Thomas P. Stafford, born September 17, 1930, from Weatherford, Oklahoma, a U.S. Air Force pilot.

James A. McDivitt, born June 10, 1929, from Chicago, Illinois, a U.S. Air Force pilot.

Edward H. White, born September 14, 1930, from San Antonio, Texas, a U.S. Air Force pilot.

John W. Young, born September 24, 1930, from San Francisco, California, a U.S. Navy pilot.

Meanwhile, Walter M. Schirra prepared for MA-8, the longest orbital mission yet scheduled and a flight which would later be called the "bull's-eye" mission. The newer astronauts were put in "basic training" for future two-man flights, and were assigned as ground assistants for the remainder of the Mercury program.

MA-8, called Sigma Seven by Schirra, was to go six orbits.

Although he was about to complete the most perfect Mercury mission to date, Schirra was one of the few of the original astronauts not too keen about the space program. His career had been going well in the United States Navy. He was a test pilot, and fiercely proud of the job he was doing on the F4H test program. This was one of the Navy's newest supersonic fighter planes.

Schirra was a contented fighter pilot, with MIG kills to his credit in Korea before he started test piloting. He loved the challenge of flying the new high-speed jet fighters in tests.

But as challenging as the F4H program was, he soon saw that space flight could be an even greater challenge. He passed the tests with one of the highest records established by any astronaut, and promptly joined the NASA program.

On October 3, 1962, he crawled into his silver space suit, was elevated to the capsule, and sealed in. The primary mission of the flight was for Schirra to make a thorough engineering evaluation of the Mercury spacecraft. He was to prove, on a somewhat longer mission, what Glenn and Carpenter had learned.

His flight was another example of the methodical "test and prove" progress of America's space scientists.

And his flight was an example of how smoothly and precisely a space shot can go, once systems have been tested and improved. Schirra blasted away from the Cape flawlessly. He was able to control his orientation with the use of much less fuel for the capsule-control jets. In fact, he used only about one third of his available fuel supply during his entire nine-hour flight. During retro-fire, he maintained his spacecraft's attitude almost perfectly.

To make a pinpoint landing on Earth from orbital flight may seem virtually impossible. Retros, for example, must be fired *exactly* 2,990 miles from the planned point of impact. Once again speaking in terms of space science, this gives the astronaut a tolerance of plus-or-minus *nothing.* The spacecraft must be held in exactly the proper attitude and the retrograde rockets must fire exactly five seconds apart, and deliver exactly the right thrust.

Walter Schirra ended his six-orbit flight, the longest American space mission to date, by floating down into the ocean just off the bow of the prime recovery ship. Photos were taken, for the first time, of a manned capsule during actual splashdown. He landed in the prime recovery area for his mission, in the Pacific Ocean northeast of Midway Island.

Like the other astronauts, Schirra had been well prepared for weightless space flight, and the problems which might result, by a machine in Cleveland, Ohio, called the "Multiple Axis Space Test Inertia Facility" or MASTIF for short. Here was a machine which appeared to have been designed by a "mad scientist" if ever one did, a horrible combination of racks and pipes and tubes which made the worst carnival ride appear to be a child's toy.

It consisted of three separate frameworks of tubular aluminum, one inside the other. The outside frame, mounted on gimbals, could pitch like a barrel tumbling end over end. Imagine what a ride inside this "barrel" could do to your stomach.

But that wasn't all, by far.

Inside this framework barrel was another cage which spun around and around like a pinwheel. Inside *this one* was *still another,* shaped a little like a Mercury capsule, which would spin on its own axis, like a spiraling football.

All astronauts made many rides inside the innermost chamber where they were revolved and tumbled and spun, *all at the same time.* And they were required, by using a control stick, to straighten out the violent motion into smooth, level, stationary attitudes.

Yes, they got "seasick," and so did the astronauts' doctor, Bill Douglas, who insisted on sampling everything the astronauts were required to do.

The comments of the astronauts on this ride always included "a cold sweat on the forehead" and "dials blurring" and "potentially violently ill." One astronaut said, "Your body feels like a tank full of loose parts and sloshing chemicals. Your liver and stomach rise and fall thirty times a minute."

Still, preparing for their own individual rides in a real spacecraft, these dedicated men would steal back to Cleveland for extra *voluntary* rides on the hated MASTIF to condition their bodies to possible tumbling in space.

From MASTIF rides, however, an interesting discovery was made about motion sickness in the average individual. Many of us suffer from this common malady, and so do some of the astronauts. First, doctors learned that it is a *change* in motion which brings on the queasy feeling in the stomach and not the motion itself. Second, the rapid motion of the eyes in an attempt to orient themselves contributes to an upset stomach. On MASTIF the eyes of the astronauts actually blurred in a manner similar to the sickening blur you might see if you tried to count fence posts from a speeding car.

Another cause of motion sickness, according to space doctors, is the up and down movement of the intestines inside the body.

The cure? If you are suffering from motion sickness, or potential motion sickness, try to make a determined effort to hold your head still. Do not attempt to focus your eyes on any moving object until the ill feeling passes. At the same time, tense your stomach muscles to keep your insides from "sloshing about."

Astronauts finally arrived at the point where they could walk away from MASTIF without a stagger, if they really tried.

In St. Louis the final Mercury capsule was being prepared. This one would complete the Mercury-Atlas program with the longest flight yet scheduled. L. Gordon Cooper's form-fitting fiber glass couch was being installed.

The room in which the capsules are assembled is more like a hospital than a factory. Pure white, it is kept even more sterile than a premature infants' ward. The doors are sealed and air conditioning removes every last speck of dust and other impurities from the air. Technicians in the room wear white surgical smocks, hats, white socks, and even white plastic shoes and so does every visitor, though there are few of these outside the astronauts themselves. Technicians assemble parts with infinite care, each of which has had a prototype tested to destruction. Most parts are never touched, since moisture from fingerprints might cause a speck of rust.

Painstaking test procedures are followed. First, a part is tested. Then another is tested. Then the two parts are fastened together, and tested as a unit. Then another part is tested, and attached to the first two parts, and the three-part unit is tested. And on and on, through a total of more than 10,000 parts and hundreds of thousands of separate tests. So critical are the demands of a space capsule that over 50 per cent of the parts purchased for installation are eventually rejected.

When these technicians are finished, they have a machine which never tires, which makes its own decisions in an emergency, and which can support a man and keep him alive and healthy in space. It is a literal machine which does exactly as it was built to do. If a mechanism were added which was supposed to fail at a certain point, it would, without a doubt, fail at that point. On mechanisms which have failed in the past, in space, the cause can invariably be traced to a man's failure instead of the machine's failure.

Then the capsule is transported to the Cape, where it is tested all over again many, many times.

On May 15, 1963, America again paused to stand before television sets and wait. The most ambitious space flight of all was scheduled to blast off from the Cape.

Due to the usual careful planning and cautious approach, this longest space flight in American history bordered on being routine.

Gordon Cooper lifted off in the morning and did not splash down until he had traveled an astounding 595,564 miles in space. He orbited the Earth twenty-two times. He flew in space for thirty-four hours and twenty and one-half minutes.

And he did *fly* in space. On his nineteenth orbit, his automatic control system ceased to function. Where this may have been a great problem earlier in the program, it no longer was. Cooper flew on, controlling his capsule for the entire remainder of the mission and through the critical retro-fire and reentry maneuvers.

He splashed down just four miles off the bow of the recovery aircraft carrier U.S.S. *Kearsarge.*

"Right on the old bazoo!" Cooper called happily from the bobbing capsule. During his mission, he had actually slept in his drifting Faith Seven for seven and one-half hours.

Cooper's flight, MA-9, proved once and for all that man could adapt himself to space and live there in reasonable comfort. Other things were learned from the Mercury program which would help in the further Gemini flights.

It was learned that conventional mass production methods would not do for the critical requirements of space flight equipment. It was learned that mistakes in space could, however, be overcome by trained astronauts.

Space could be, and had been, conquered.

The Mercury program had cost the taxpayers $348,000,000 according to NASA. In about two years, six men had gone into space, four of them for orbital rides. Many, many other non-manned space objects had been launched into orbit. Not a single spaceman had been so much as injured during the entire program if such matters as John Glenn's skinned knuckles (which he received firing his hatch at the end of his mission) were overlooked.

On October 18, 1963, NASA introduced a third group of astronauts with an even younger average age of thirty-one. Their education was best of the three groups. The third group included one man with a doctor's degree and six with master's degrees. The strict physical requirements were relaxed slightly (though not very much, to be sure) and the requirement that the applicant must have test-pilot experience was reduced. Two women applied for the third group, but failed to meet the new educational demands. Rather than being pilots (though all had flying training) three of the men were career scientists.

In all, over 700 people had volunteered to become a part of the third group.

Fourteen were finally selected:

Edwin E. Aldrin, Jr., born January 20, 1930, from Glen Ridge, New Jersey, a U.S. Air Force pilot.

William A. Anders, born October 17, 1933, in Hong Kong, China, a pilot in the U.S. Air Force.

Charles A. Bassett, born December 30, 1931, from Dayton, Ohio, a U.S. Air Force pilot. (Died in plane crash, February 28, 1966.)

Alan L. Bean, born March 15, 1932, from Wheeler, Texas, a U.S. Navy pilot.

Eugene A. Cernan, born March 14, 1934, from Chicago, Illinois, a U.S. Air Force pilot.

Roger B. Chaffee, born February 15, 1935, from Grand Rapids, Michigan, a U.S. Navy pilot.

Michael Collins, born October 31, 1930, in Rome, Italy, a U.S. Air Force pilot.

R. Walter Cunningham, born March 16, 1932, from Creston, Iowa, a civilian.

Donn F. Eisele, born June 23, 1930, from Columbus, Ohio, a U.S. Air Force pilot.

Theodore C. Freeman, born February 18, 1930, from Haverford, Pennsylvania, a U.S. Air Force pilot. (Died in a jet plane crash, the first astronaut lost—though not in a space flight.)

Richard F. Gordon, Jr., born October 5, 1929, from Seattle, Washington, a U.S. Navy pilot.

Russell L. Schweickart, born October 25, 1935, from Neptune, New Jersey, a civilian.

David R. Scott, born June 6, 1932, from San Antonio, Texas, a U.S. Air Force pilot.

Clifton C. Williams, Jr., born September 26, 1932, from Mobile, Alabama, a U.S. Marine Corps pilot.

By 1970, the names of these men will be bywords in our language. Some of them will surely land on the moon, and go beyond.

For they are the Apollo spacemen, the spacemen of the future.

November 22, 1963, was a black day in the history of our country, and a black day for our space effort. Our young president, John F. Kennedy, the man who had pushed the exploration of space forward, was assassinated. Within the week, the name Cape Canaveral was changed, in his honor, to Cape Kennedy.

It was a fitting tribute to a man who could see the future of America in space, for from Cape Kennedy and nearby Merritt Island our spacemen would blast off in as-yet-undreamed-of rockets to conquer the universe. Even today, rockets such as the gigantic Saturn V, many times the size of the original Redstones, are being readied to carry men into deep space. With power difficult to imagine, they will thunder away from Cape Kennedy. The size of skyscrapers, they will shake the earth of Florida as their mighty engines ignite.

The Cape is on a spit of land on the east coast of the state of Florida, nine miles north of Cocoa Beach. Merritt Island is immediately next to it, between the Cape and the mainland along the Banana River. These strips of sand contain the most amazing complex of missile-launching areas in the world. From simple guide rails for small rockets through complicated launching pads for larger boosters to the gigantic Saturn pad, larger than *forty* football fields and containing the largest single building in the world (a cubic capacity of *four complete Empire State Buildings*), the Cape area is a humming beehive of constant activity. Trucks the size of a baseball diamond move rockets about. The whole area, 102,000 acres, is known officially as the John F. Kennedy Space Center, and from here are launched not only our manned rockets, but many, many unmanned satellites as well.

The Cape has factories, docks, and administrative buildings and thousands of employees. This exciting area never sleeps.

A tremendous new rocket had been moved into place on its pad, and on April 8, 1964, a new thunder reverberated across the

Cape, as this newcomer blasted away. Another lifted off later, and then the mighty Titan II was declared qualified for manned flight. At the same time, in St. Louis, the new spacecraft shape and structure was verified.

This one was similar to the Mercury capsule, yet different. It was larger, and had *two* inset windows. Inside it was far more sophisticated, with equipment undreamed of during the early Mercury flights. And inside were *two* form-fitting couches.

This was the long-planned Gemini capsule, named from the twin stars Castor and Pollux in the third constellation of the zodiac. It would carry two men into space.

It was mated to the mighty Titan.

Where the Redstone could lift 2000 pounds into suborbital flight, and the Atlas 2000 pounds into orbital flight, the Titan II had enough thrust to place *6000* pounds in orbit. It was a magnificently colored rocket with a giant U.S. Air Force insignia blazed on its side about halfway up.

The first Gemini flight was scheduled.

5

Two terms, although important to the Mercury program, are even more important in the Gemini flights. They are *apogee* and *perigee.* For maneuvers such as docking with another object in space, these measured altitudes must be correct.

Apogee is the point farthest from the Earth in the orbit of a space object. This is the highest altitude the spacecraft attains in its flight around the world. As you know, many orbits are not perfectly circular, but are oval, or "egg-shaped."

Perigee is the point nearest the Earth during orbital flight.

If you hear the term *perihelion,* you will know that this is the point nearest the sun in the path of a solar orbit object. America has sent many unmanned objects into a solar orbit.

Since we are about to progress farther and farther from Earth, let us try to imagine the actual size of space. Certain terms will be helpful here.

Earth's atmosphere is present in greatly diminishing quantities up to over 100 miles in altitude. Here, *Cislunar Space* begins. This is the area from the very limit of our own atmosphere on to the moon. This is the area which the Apollo spacemen will explore.

From the moon to the outer limits of the planets in our own solar system is called *Interplanetary Space.* This extends to a distance of over *ten billion* miles, beyond Pluto. *Interstellar Space* extends on from there to *Intergalactic Space* and the distances become astounding. The breaking point between these last two, for example, is over 100,000,000,000,000,000 (100 quadrillion) miles from the surface of the Earth. Intergalactic Space just goes on from there. Man has not yet determined how far, or if there is an end to it at all.

To give you a more graphic idea of some of these distances which we will one day in the future travel, imagine this page with a drawing of the Earth upon it. Now let us properly scale a drawing of these distances as we would scale a drawing of a new sports car, only in this case we will make one inch equal *one thousand miles.*

Where, on the page, would we draw Pluto, the last known planet in our own system? In our own lifetime we will very likely visit Pluto.

You're right. Pluto would never fit on this page, even with a scale of only one inch equalling 1000 miles. Keeping in mind that we are still only speaking of Interplanetary Space, one of the nearer measurements, Pluto would have to be drawn *forty miles away* from this page.

To include the nearest star to Earth, a very close neighbor in space terms, we would have to make a drawing many, many thousands of miles away. The whole Earth is not large enough to include such a drawing, at this scale. This nearby star, Proxima Centauri, is actually 25 *trillion* miles from Earth.

Such distances are difficult to imagine.

Continued exploration was planned. Gemini-Titan Three was scheduled for only three orbits of the Earth. This would be the initial effort in the Gemini program, and would serve to man-test the Gemini two-man capsule in space, with its advanced equipment, and the Titan booster. If all went well on this flight, GT-4 would be more dramatic. It would go for a much longer time in space, and it would have EVA as a part of its flight plan. Extra-Vehicular Activity, where a man would *leave* the capsule and drift about in space outside.

The proposed schedule then moved to Gemini-Titan Five, which would spend *eight days* in space. GT-6 was planned as the first of the "docking" flights, where astronauts would attempt to join their craft with another in space. GT-7 was planned as an endurance-record smasher. On this one, astronauts would spend *fourteen days* in orbit. Then, during GT-8, one astronaut would leave the capsule on an EVA maneuver, and stay outside, untethered part of the time, for an entire orbit around the Earth.

Further GT missions were tentatively planned, depending

President Kennedy is briefed by Mercury Astronaut Walter M. Schirra, Jr. at Complex 14 at Cape Canaveral.

The National Aeronautics and Space Administration introduced 14 new astronauts at a news conference, bringing to 30 the total assigned to Manned Spacecraft Center programs. Standing left to right: Michael Collins, Capt., USAF; R. Walter Cunningham, civilian; Donn F. Eisele, Capt., USAF; Theodore C. Freeman, Capt., USAF; Richard F. Gordon, Jr., LCDR, USN; Russell L. Schweikart, civilian; David R. Scott, Capt., USAF; Clifton C. Williams, Jr., Capt., USMC. Seated, left to right: Edwin E. Aldrin, Jr., Major, USAF; William A. Anders, Capt., USAF; Charles A. Bassett, II, Capt., USAF; Alan L. Bean, Lt., USN; Eugene A. Cernan, Lt., USN; Roger B. Chaffee, Lt., USN.

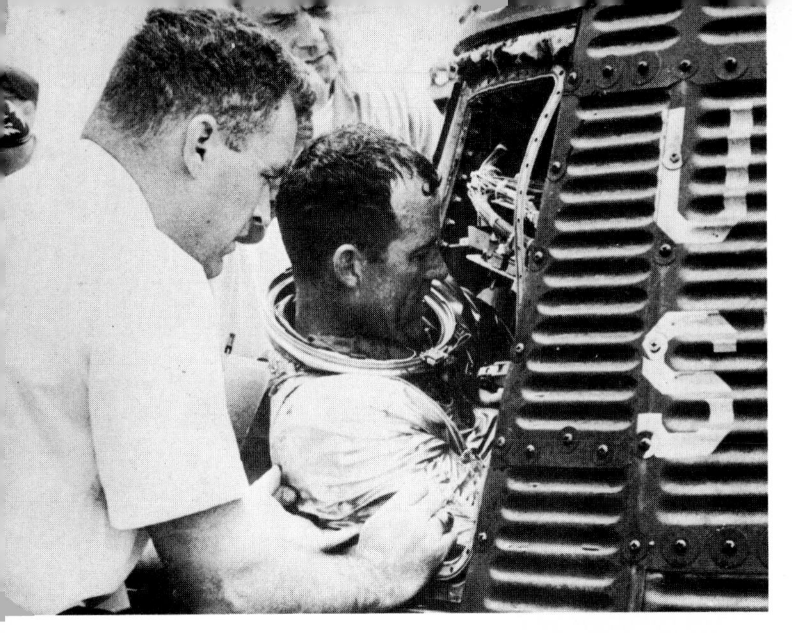

Astronaut L. Gordon Cooper, Jr., begins to emerge from Faith Seven on the deck of the carrier Kearsarge, assisted by Dr. Richard Pollard of the Aeromedical Operations Office.

Cape Canaveral, Florida—Astronaut L. Gordon Cooper, Jr., leaves the transfer van for his ride up the gantry elevator to the 11th deck where he will be inserted into the spacecraft for his 22-orbit mission.

Cape Canaveral, Florida—Mercury Control—The Faith Seven spacecraft shown on the world map has just passed over the Zanzibar tracking station on its 16th orbit.

President Kennedy says goodbye to L. Gordon Cooper on the steps of the north portico of the White House. Shortly before, the President had pinned the National Aeronautics and Space Administration's Distinguished Service Medal on the astronaut.

The "white room" atop the rocket at the Cape. Technicians prepare the spacecraft for the blast off.

The Gemini "clean room" at McDonnell Aircraft.

upon need and depending upon the state of the Apollo program at that time. If initial docking maneuvers went well, for example, fewer Gemini missions would be needed, for that is one of the prime studies of the Gemini program.

It was an ambitious schedule, considering that we had never put two men in space at the same time, but not an unsafe schedule, and certainly not an impossible one. We had the vehicle and we had the spacecraft.

And the men who would fly the missions were ready, or being trained, each of them competing intensely with the others for the privilege of going.

Astronaut Gus Grissom was selected as the command pilot of the first two-man ride in space, and he promptly named the capsule The Unsinkable Molly Brown after a well-known play and motion picture . . . and for obvious reasons (if you recall what happened to Mercury-Redstone Four). John W. Young, of the second group of astronauts, would be the pilot.

For the first time possible, an "old pro" astronaut would be used, a man who had already flown once in space. Grissom was happy and proud, and redoubled his study and training schedule so that he would be perfectly prepared for this advanced effort.

New tools were being readied, and would need testing under actual space conditions. Take a simple wrench to tighten a nut, for example. We've all changed a tire on a car, or at least observed this action. It isn't difficult at all. When it comes time to tighten the wheel nuts, we just tighten them.

Not in space, though.

Every time an astronaut exerts a pressure in one direction, he turns in another direction. If he tried to tighten a wheel nut in space, he would spin his whole body in the opposite direction the instant he applied pressure.

This is Newton's third law of motion. For every action there is an equal and opposite reaction. On Earth we can overcome this reaction by bracing our feet, thus "absorbing" the opposite force. But in space there is no gravity to help "anchor" the man with the wrench, so he reacts in a perfectly opposite manner to any force he applies.

The new space wrench is only one of many changes in tools designed for space use. Appearing much like a power hand drill, the wrench has a built-in reaction absorber. When the astronaut presses the trigger, the motor (battery driven) near the handle compresses a spring with a brief twist. As the spring expands, it turns a hollow cylinder that surrounds it. Compression and release of the spring, 1800 times per second, occurs alternately, and this rapid rotation and counter-rotation of the cylinder and motor all but cancel each other out. The astronaut can tighten or loosen a nut without being jerked about himself.

Grissom and Young, meanwhile, continued to prepare for their flight with a specific list of experiments they were to conduct. They would demonstrate the manned orbital capability of the new Gemini spacecraft and at the same time continue to qualify both the Titan booster and the worldwide communications and tracking network.

They would make a minute evaluation of the interior of the Gemini capsule and its effect on the crew, in space.

They would test the ability of the spacecraft to maneuver in space, using the OAMS, the Orbital Attitude and Maneuvering Propulsion System. They would demonstrate the ability of the spacecraft to hit a preselected target in the splashdown area. They would thoroughly test all spacecraft systems including the crew-station controls and displays, the environmental controls, the guidance controls, all electrical power systems, all communications and tracking systems, all instrumentation, and food, water, and waste management. They would also evaluate the new space suits, slightly different from the Mercury suits.

Two scientific experiments were placed aboard the Gemini. One would test the effect of zero gravity on sea urchin eggs to determine whether cellular development is affected. The other experiment was to determine whether the absence of normal gravity increases, reduces, or has no effect on the radiation-induced changes in the blood cells of man.

Grissom was also to attempt to change the apogee and perigee of his spacecraft with capsule controls. At about 300,000 feet, during reentry, astronaut Young was to inject approximately fifteen pounds of water into the ionized sheath surrounding the spacecraft, at the same time attempting to transmit through this sheath. Remember the communications "blackout"? This experiment was designed to overcome this period of lack of communication with the spacecraft.

As you can see, astronauts do not merely float around in space, but are given much difficult work to do, and not much time to do it in. All of these tasks and experiments would be accomplished in only three orbits, but they were necessary for the success of future Gemini missions.

We knew, for example, that we were sending longer missions aloft in the near future. Suppose an absence of gravity *did* have an adverse effect on the blood cells? It turns out it didn't, but if it did, we wanted to know it *before* sending men up for long periods of weightlessness.

GT-3 was postponed from March 22, 1965, to March 23, 1965, but not due to a fault in the men or systems. Ranger Nine, a lunar photographic mission, was scheduled at the same time, and both launches were to use the same radio command guidance system. Always cautious with the lives of astronauts, NASA's manned space flight procedures require that all systems be "locked up" twenty-four hours before any flight. They would not permit the command guidance system to be used immediately prior to a manned flight, without the normal long countdown and test procedures. So Ranger Nine went, and on March 23, Gemini-Titan Three blasted off.

Again, the entire flight was transmitted by television, as it was occurring. The public heard conversations between the two astronauts in space, as the men talked. They were aware that the sea urchin egg experiment was not going well. They were aware of the position of the spacecraft at every moment. They tensely waited with space scientists through the retro-fire and reentry sequence.

They knew that The Unsinkable Molly Brown did not sink, as Liberty Bell had, and that the mission had been another success. America had two more space heroes. The second group of astronauts had been well represented by pilot Young, who worked smoothly and with great precision in space.

This group was to be well represented again on June 3, 1965, when two of its members captured the interest of the whole world during a dramatic experiment in space.

"This is Gemini control. Four hours and twenty-four minutes into the mission." The voice from the ground controller had a note of urgency. "The Hawaii station has just established contact and the pilot, Jim McDivitt, advises the cabin has been depressurized. It is reading zero. We are standing by for a GO from Hawaii to open the hatch . . . White has opened the door. He has stood up, and it's a most relaxed period. McDivitt reports that White is standing in his seat . . ."

Science fiction? Not at all. This was Gemini-Titan Four, the second two-man capsule to be launched from the Cape.

One of America's most exciting, dangerous space adventures was beginning.

The launch had been, as usual, near routine. Two hours before zero the second set of Gemini twins arrived at the pad. They were Jim McDivitt and Ed White, both from the second group of astronauts. Dressed in their Gemini space suits, they took the elevator to the capsule level of the gantry and at 7:32 A.M. the twin hatches were sealed.

The only problem during countdown came with a balky erector tower, which was supposed to smoothly tip over and down to the ground alongside the Titan. An electric motor was replaced in the tower and things moved along. At T minus 30, the pad was cleared of all technicians in preparation for the launch.

At 10:16 the countdown reached ignition and the rocket trembled with power. The hold-down clamps released, and it started upward.

"OK, Jim, have a good flight," came the voice of Flight Director Chris Kraft. It was calm and full of confidence. Four years before, when Al Shepard's Redstone lifted off, the air had been charged with tension, but now rocket shots were proven. No trouble was anticipated, and none was encountered.

Soon the voice of Jim McDivitt came from the space capsule.

"Roll initiated."

"Roger," from the ground.

For an instant, as the rocket streaked through the higher altitudes above Earth, it left behind a tortured contrail. Then it disappeared. Moving at 25,745 feet per second, it was only 11 feet per second off a perfect insertion speed.

For the first time in the history of the space program, the new Manned Spaceflight Center in Houston, Texas, took control of the mission. Until then, control had always been maintained from the Cape. Now all space flights are controlled from Houston, shifted there from the Cape immediately after lift-off.

Gemini Four was launched with several planned experiments, but the experiment that had captured the fancy of the world, and even at that moment had Americans standing by their TV sets, was the EVA—Extra-Vehicular Activity.

An astronaut would leave the spacecraft's protection and enter the hostile environment of outer space. There, kept alive only by his space suit and with a pure gold visor across his face to stop the blinding rays of the sun, he would "walk in space."

An initial experiment, though, would be an attempt by the astronauts to approach their booster by guiding their capsule about in space. But the old problem of fuel again presented itself, and the experiment was cancelled. Too much precious fuel would be burned up in the attempt at rendezvous and so the booster, "space object 1391," was forgotten. Two days later it would fall and burn up over the Atlantic Ocean.

EVA, originally scheduled for the second revolution around the world, was temporarily postponed, and Americans held their breath. They wanted this maneuver, and they wanted it exhibited plainly, as it was happening, on TV sets around the world. The astronauts were still completing primary preparations, and McDivitt, the command pilot, wanted everything completed and ready before the "space walk" was attempted.

Gemini Four was completing its third orbit, nearing the west coast of the United States, when the cabin hatch was finally opened to the near-vacuum of space. Communications were with the Kauai, Hawaii, station. Altitude was 120 miles.

Speed, relative to the surface of the Earth, was *five* miles per *second.*

"All systems on the ground look good," informed Hawaii.

"You're having him get out?" asked Houston, in direct communication with Hawaii.

"Roger, Flight, we're GO . . ." answered Hawaii CapCom.

"Tell him we're ready to have him get out when he is," acknowledged Houston.

The voice came down from space. "He's ready to egress right now," called McDivitt.

The two astronauts had slowly depressurized their space cabin, at the same time assuring themselves that their space suits were functioning. The space suits would pressurize, if all went as planned, and maintain a life-sustaining atmosphere inside. This done, the hatch over Ed White's head had been opened, and White stood slowly in his seat. Half his body was in the capsule, half was out in space. Reaching behind, he picked up an odd looking "space gun" with two opposite reaching "barrels."

This gun, it was hoped, would enable him to maneuver about at the end of a long tether which would keep him attached to the capsule. Through the line would flow electricity for his suit, communications, and oxygen. On his lower chest was a second oxygen unit for emergency use. This one, in case the tether malfunctioned, would give him about nine more minutes of oxygen which was enough time, according to plans, for him to return to the capsule and seal it.

Americans listened to the voices from control, and from space, in "real time." This is a space term meaning "as it is happening, with no delay." Another example of space scientists' confidence in the program.

The voices could have been delayed by seconds or minutes in order for sections of conversation to be removed, but they were not. Everybody heard exactly what was happening, as it happened.

White activated his gun and floated up from the capsule.

He turned at the end of the tether, paused for a moment, then saluted Jim McDivitt, his command pilot.

This done, he spoke, and his voice was jubilant. Millions of Americans listened.

"This is the greatest experience . . . it's just tremendous . . . absolutely no disorientation . . . I'm looking right down, and it looks like we're coming up on the coast of California, and I'm going in slow rotation to the right . . ."

The voices continued as the spacecraft flashed across the United States.

McDivitt: "One thing about it, when Ed gets out there and starts whipping around it sure makes the spacecraft tough to control . . ."

White: "I'm going to work on getting some pictures, Jim."

McDivitt: "OK, get out in front where I can see you again . . . Where are you?"

White: "Right out in front now. I don't have the control I had anymore . . . There's no difficulty in recontacting the spacecraft . . . particularly in trying to move back . . . I'm very thankful in having the experience to be first . . ."

McDivitt: "Ed, will you please roll around? Right now we're pointing just about straight down to the ground."

White: "OK, now I'm taking a look back at the adaptor. I'm looking back there. The thrusters are clean. (White, at this point, was moving around the capsule, examining it, in space.) The sun in space is not blinding but it's quite nice. I'm coming back down on the spacecraft. I can sit out here and see the whole California coast."

Flight Surgeon: "Flight, this is Surgeon. The data here looks great."

Flight Director: "How's his EKG (electrocardiogram)?"

Flight Surgeon: "It looks great, Flight. He's just ripping along here at great rate."

McDivitt: "You smeared up my windshield, you dirty dog! You see how it's all smeared up there?"

White (chuckling): "Yep!"

White was outside the spacecraft, peering in through the command pilot's window, grinning at McDivitt . . . and having a wonderful time.

And the answers to the basic questions asked by scientists were being given by McDivitt and White. Can man maneuver on his own outside a spacecraft? Yes. Can he do it without physical harm or strain? Yes.

And Ed White was finding the whole experiment great fun.

McDivitt: "Looks like there's a coating on the outside and you've rubbed it off. That's apparently what you've done."

Then . . .

McDivitt to CapCom: "Gus, this is Jim. Got any messages for us?"

CapCom (Gus Grissom): "Gemini Four. Get back in."

It was the saddest message of the flight for Ed White.

McDivitt: "OK . . ."

White: "OK, I'm on top of it right now."

McDivitt: "OK, you're right on top. Come on in, then."

White: "All right."

McDivitt: "Ed, the Flight Director says get back in."

White: "OK."

McDivitt (almost pleading): "They want you back in."

White: "Coming in."

He stalled a little longer, knowing that he must return to the space ship, but wanting to prolong his experience outside the craft.

McDivitt: "I'll put the gun up."

White: "I'll open the door and come through here."

McDivitt: "OK. Let's not lose this camera now. (Earlier, an unattached space glove had drifted up from White's seat and through the open hatch. Chances are, it is still orbiting the Earth, probably lost forever.) I don't quite have it. A little bit more. OK, I've got it . . . come on. Let's get back in here before it gets dark."

Ed White returned to the space cabin, and dropped slowly through the hatch. He had been outside for twenty-one and one-half minutes, a record which would stand for many months.

The space walk was not, however, without one final complication. White's hatch refused to seal properly, a potentially deadly problem. Certainly the space suits of the astronauts would protect them while in space, but what about during reentry?

And so McDivitt performed another "first." With tools provided for emergencies, he repaired the hatch lock and sealed it correctly while the capsule drifted in space. Yes, man could work in space—and had.

This problem also created a humorous situation later in the flight. The astronauts, scheduled for a four-day mission in space, had planned to reopen the hatch from time to time to dispose of materials no longer needed, including leftover foods. Because of the hatch problem, they did not again attempt to open the cabin, and the interior soon began to look like the interior of a garbage can, with the only difference being that in space the garbage would not lie quietly at the bottom of the container, but floated around freely.

These American spacemen faced this new unexpected "hazard" calmly, and fell into a schedule of working, eating, and sleeping. They had eleven on-board experiments scheduled, including the docking and the EVA. Medical experiments such as exercise, EKG's, and blood-pressure readings were conducted periodically. They measured radiation and the magnetic field of the Earth from space. Photo experiments included synoptic weather and synoptic Earth limb pictures.

At one point in space, over southeast Asia, they could see *seven countries* at the same time.

On the second day, they set a new space-endurance record for Americans in space. This record, however, would not stand long.

On the fourth day, by then piling record on record for space endurance, they faced their first serious problem since the hatch-lock problem. On the forty-ninth orbit a computer designed to position the spacecraft for reentry malfunctioned. A manually controlled, rolling reentry was decided upon.

Nearing Hawaii on the sixty-second orbit, the spacemen prepared themselves for their return to Earth. Floating debris was packaged and tied down as much as possible. The nation below waited.

The retrograde rockets fired on schedule, and the spacecraft slowed and began its burning reentry.

"There goes Florida on your side," shouted one of the men.

"We're RED HOT, Jim!" exclaimed Ed White.

"Sit back and relax," answered command pilot McDivitt.

Then, in a moment, "Look at the paint coming off on the window!"

Finally, from high in the sky, but no longer space, "Does that parachute look GREAT!!"

They splashed down at 12:13 on June 7.

Seven minutes later they were picked up, flown to the aircraft carrier *Wasp,* and at 12:55 Jim McDivitt opened his hatch and breathed deeply.

Both men were in excellent condition. They had proven that man could work and live in space without suffering ill effects provided the environment was carefully controlled (though they both complained later of minor sleeping problems).

The first walk in space had been successful. More would follow.

But first, America set out to establish an endurance record that would leave no doubt she had conquered space completely.

A Mercury spaceman was chosen as command pilot, a Gemini spaceman as pilot. Apollo spacemen were still in rigorous training.

Eight days in space was the proposed mission length.

Jubilantly, Gordon Cooper (another "old pro") and Charles Conrad prepared for their mission in Gemini-Titan Five. Everything seemed to be moving faster. Where not too many months ago, space flights were widely scattered, with months of preparation necessary, now they seemed to be coming far more rapidly, one right after the other.

The target date was August, only two months after the flight of McDivitt and White.

6

GT-5, scheduled to become the longest space mission in history, very nearly became one of the shortest. Before launch, the flight seemed to be dogged with bad luck. The two astronauts were ready and eager, but the spacecraft was not.

Then, immediately prior to launch, the mission was twice postponed. Fuel cells were low on fuel, liquid hydrogen kept boiling away uselessly, telemetering equipment would suddenly, without apparent reason, malfunction. There was a fire near the launch pad. Thunderstorms boiled overhead.

Finally everything seemed to clear up and the launch countdown progressed smoothly on the morning of August 21, 1965.

Surprisingly, when it finally came it was the most perfect launch in history. Without a single hold in the final countdown, the missile thundered away exactly on schedule. In the nose capsule, Cooper and Conrad reported all was well.

"You are go . . . you are GO!" shouted Jim McDivitt happily. After serving as command pilot on the last Gemini flight, he was the capsule communicator on this one.

Fifty-six minutes after lift-off, the first important experiment started . . . a change in apogee. Cooper activated the thrusters on the spacecraft and the orbit was changed.

Then came a very important experiment, the REP maneuver.

Stowed in the capsule's broad end, with small boosters of its own, was the Radar Evaluation Pod, a 76-pound package with bright flashing lights and radar transponders. This package was to be an orbiting target to which the capsule would be steered by the astronauts. This would be a big step toward later, full-scale docking with another spacecraft. It was an experiment the scientists on the ground desperately wanted completed.

But even before it could begin, the calm voice of astronaut

Cooper, in an almost routine way, reported a situation which would prove critical in a few moments. The pressure in the fuel-cell oxygen-supply tanks, he informed CapCom, was falling. A gauge which should have read 800 to 900 pounds per square inch was dropping fast. The fuel cells, untried in space, were the heart of the Gemini Five capsule, furnishing power not only to the communications and computer systems, but also to the very important environmental-control systems.

Unlike conventional batteries (used on previous space flights), these new space-age fuel cells could provide power in the form of electricity for as long as they received fuel. Batteries run down eventually; fuel cells do not. They were being tested on Gemini Five for later use on long missions into deep space. But they were, apparently, failing, and the mission's success was uncertain. If things got worse, the lives of the two astronauts could hang in the balance.

Gemini streaked into its second orbit. Although REP was released from the spacecraft, it was decided that too much power would be consumed in tracking it, so the experiment was scratched. Meanwhile, Air Force planes were hurrying into position over an emergency splashdown area in the Pacific Ocean. A Navy destroyer and an oiler in the vicinity were ordered to stand by for possible pick-up of astronauts.

Flight Director Chris Kraft listened to Cooper as he spoke from space. "We've decided we're going to have to either reenter early, or else power down."

Kraft immediately ordered power down. Only absolutely critical power systems would be used in the spacecraft, in an effort to conserve the dwindling power supply. Back-up batteries were on board, but they had only enough power stored to provide electricity for a reentry.

"We're working on a new flight plan for you," Kraft notified Cooper.

In space there was only an ominous quiet. The astronauts

had turned off the radar, radio, computer, and even some of the environmental-control systems. The very critical systems they could not live without were consuming only thirteen amperes of electricity—exactly what the failing fuel cells were providing.

Americans, by their radios and TV sets, waited tensely to see what decision would be made.

Chris Kraft called the capsule. "What is your pressure reading now?"

"One hundred and twenty-five pounds," was the answer from space. Far too low.

But the rate of decrease was slowing. Still, the pressure continued to fall, if slower than before. One hundred pounds per square inch . . . ninety pounds . . . eighty pounds . . . and lower. If the pressure fell to twenty pounds per square inch, the cells would be producing no electricity, and the capsule would have to be switched to the back-up batteries just to keep the astronauts alive. But they could produce only enough power for reentry, and not one ampere more.

During the next pass the astronauts were called even though their own transmitter had been turned off.

"If you have had a significant pressure rise, please turn on your transmitter and acknowledge," said the ground controller.

No answer came from space. No significant pressure increase had been noted.

The pressure, according to ground instruments, had leveled off at seventy pounds. This was just enough to continue the critical systems on the capsule, providing it didn't start to fall again. A carefully considered decision was in the making. The sixth orbit was approaching. Beyond this orbit, no convenient landing place would be available for many, many hours, since the spacecraft would be orbiting over inhospitable areas. Or, the craft could be brought down at the end of the sixth orbit in the emergency area being readied, though this would be a touch-and-go recovery at best in an unprepared location.

CapCom called command pilot Cooper. "I would like your

opinion on going through another day under these (drifting flight) circumstances."

"We might as well try it," replied Cooper calmly.

"OK," answered CapCom, "we will look at this thing for another orbit."

Go . . . or no go? Chris Kraft, the flight director, would make the decision. The astronauts were ready to try, in spite of the low output from the fuel cells, but it was Kraft's final decision to make. He consulted with engineers and NASA directors. Never before had we failed to complete a planned mission.

He deliberated, checking on the capsule condition at the same time. Flying power down, all critical systems were still functioning normally. The astronauts were in no immediate danger.

Kraft said, "GO!" with confidence, and Americans cheered.

But for Cooper and Conrad it would apparently be a long, silent flight through space. No power was available for the experiments, nor for the easy, relaxed banter with the ground station that marked previous flights. They used their transmitter, and other power-consuming equipment, only when absolutely necessary. And they had seven days to go.

But then, inexplicably, the trickle of oxygen to the fuel cells started to build up. Gradually, pound by pound, over the first days of the mission, the pressure increased. Systems, one by one, were switched back on and by the third day in space everything was functioning as planned. Since the REP's batteries had, by then, long since failed, an attempt was made to rendezvous with an imaginary object in space through the use of computers. The rendezvous succeeded, thus accomplishing one of the prime experiments of the mission.

"One of the biggest things we've learned," announced Kraft, "is being able to pick a point in space, seek it out and find it. And it appears we have a real good hack (space talk for "grasp") on what we can do with Gemini Six in getting a spacecraft in the right position to carry out the terminal phase of rendezvous."

It was a far, far cry from Alan Shepard's MR-3.

Things perked up aboard the spacecraft with the increase of power, and a lighter, happier attitude prevailed (though the two spacemen again found trouble sleeping in the little capsule).

At one point, McDivitt chided Astronaut Conrad, saying, "You sure do talk a lot."

Conrad shot back, "What do you want me to do, sing a song?"

"Think you can?" asked McDivitt from the ground.

Command Pilot Cooper interrupted with a stern warning. "He sings off-key."

But quickly, and yes, off-key, Conrad sang a ditty which started . . .

"Over the ocean,
Over the blue,
Here's Gemini Five,
Singing to you."

More important events took place during the flight of Gemini Five. For the first time an astronaut in space witnessed the firing of a missile from the ground. Both astronauts saw launchings. Conrad, who has 20/15 vision, also saw the contrails of jet airplanes in the atmosphere below, and the streets of cities, and the wakes of ships in the ocean.

An all-time endurance record was approaching, and as the mission exceeded 119 hours, 6 minutes, the record fell. More than two years earlier, Soviet Cosmonaut Valery F. Bykovsky had set that record in an 81-orbit flight in *Vostok V*.

"How does it feel for the U.S. to be a world-record holder, Gordo?" asked CapCom.

"At last, huh?" was the laconic reply.

The flight bored on, and another problem cropped up. The fuel cells in the spacecraft were generating electricity by mixing hydrogen with oxygen. Do you know what the by-product of these two gases is? Right, water. Where do you store an excess of such water after planned storage areas have been filled? More and more

Rear view of a Gemini Spacecraft . . . the equipment adaptor ring.

Gemini spacecraft interior through fish-eye lens.

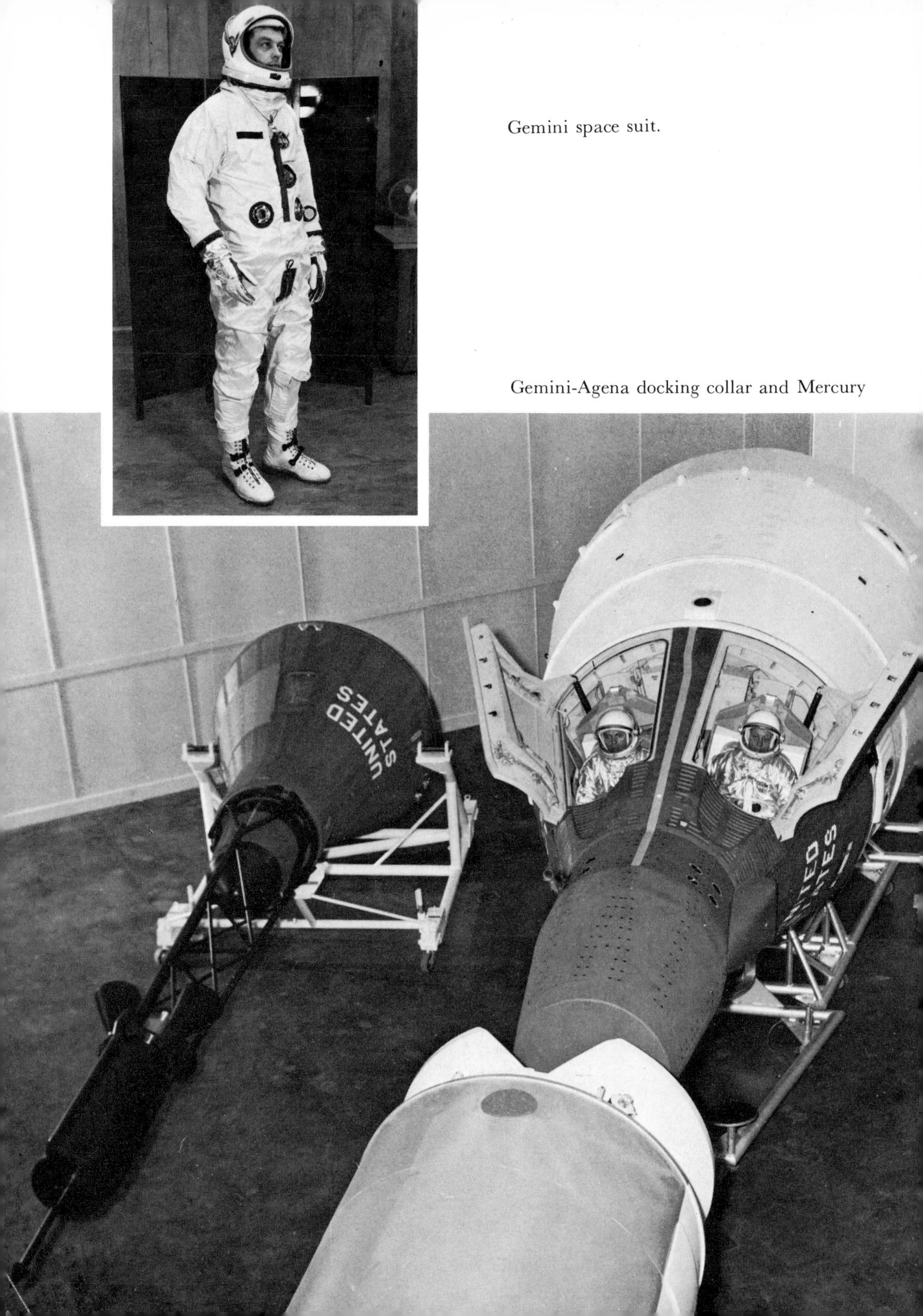

Gemini space suit.

Gemini-Agena docking collar and Mercury

Cape Kennedy, Florida—Astronauts James A. McDivitt, left, and Edward H. White II use a celestial navigation aid to study the locations of the constellations and other celestial bodies before their Gemini Four space mission. The small globe in the center represents the earth, and star locations are on the large outer globe.

Pre-Launch—Astronauts James A. McDivitt (left), command pilot for the Gemini Four space flight, and Edward H. White II, pilot, are seen here inside the Gemini Four spacecraft prior to liftoff. McDonnell Aircraft and NASA personnel make final checks on the spacecraft and astronauts before closing the hatches. This operation takes place in the white room atop the Titan launch vehicle. The Gemini Four flight was scheduled as a 4-day, 62-revolution mission. White was scheduled to perform extravehicular activities during an early revolution.

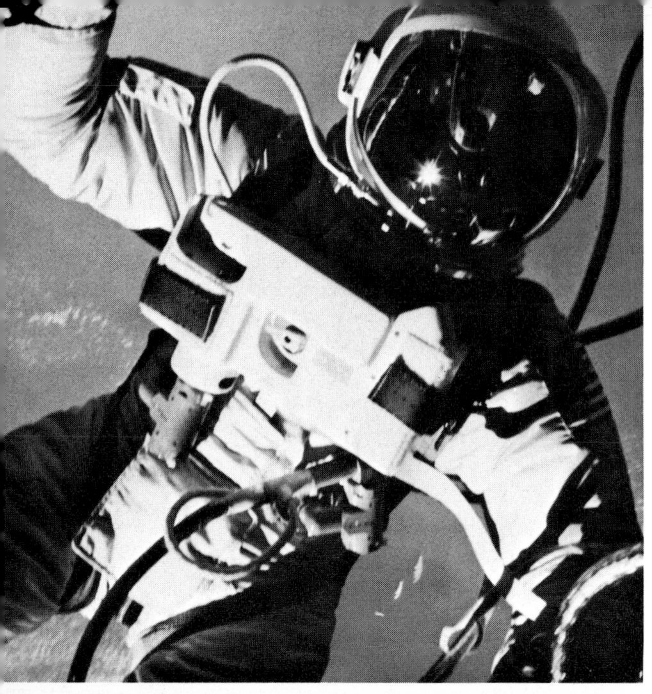

EVA—Astronaut Edward H. White II, pilot for the Gemini-Titan Four space flight, floats in the zero gravity of space outside the Gemini Four spacecraft. In the background is the earth visible beyond the cloud cover. White is attached to the spacecraft by a 25-foot umbilical line and a 23-foot tether line, both wrapped in gold tape to form one cord. Astronaut James A. McDivitt, command pilot, remained inside the spacecraft during White's extravehicular activity.

Cape Kennedy as seen from the Gemini Four spacecraft. The photograph was taken with a hand-held Hasselblad camera. The Saturn Five launch complex can be seen in the upper portion of the Cape Area.

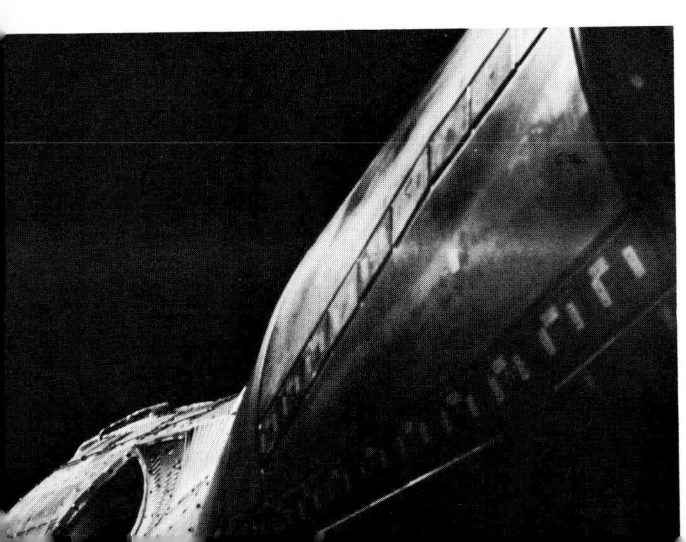

Astronaut Edward H. White II, pilot of the Gemini-Titan Four flight, took this picture of the Gemini Four spacecraft during his extravehicular activity on the third orbit of the mission. This is the first picture taken of a spacecraft while in orbit from outside the spacecraft.

Downrange Recovery Area, Atlantic Ocean—Astronauts James A. McDivitt (on deck) and Edward H. White II, (emerging from helicopter) are welcomed aboard the aircraft carrier the USS Wasp. Shown here are (from left) John Stonesifer, (white shirt) Landing and Recovery Division, Manned Spacecraft Center; Ben James, Public Affairs Office, MSC; and Dr. Howard Minners (at far right), Center Medical Office, MSC.

Astronaut Edward H. White II, pilot, and James A. McDivitt, command pilot, walk down the red carpet spread along the deck of the Aircraft Carrier Wasp following their recovery by helicopter. The astronauts received an enthusiastic reception by personnel aboard the carrier.

These photographs of the National Aeronautics and Space Administration's Gemini Six spacecraft were taken through the hatch window of the Gemini Six spacecraft during the rendezvous and station-keeping maneuvers at an altitude of approximately 160 miles on December 15, 1965.

Apollo Service Module Mockup—This model shows a portion of the Apollo spacecraft that will contain the main rocket engine and the propellant supply for maneuvers to and from the moon. Standing by the flaring skirt of the engine are North American Aviation and Aerojet-General Corporation rocket engineers. The start-stop engine will produce 21,900 pounds of thrust to keep Apollo on course to and from the moon and to perform many other missions.

The three sections of the Apollo spacecraft. Left is the Command Module, center is the LEM, and right is the Service Module.

water was being generated, and mission controllers feared that the fluid might eventually back up into the fuel cells and knock them out once and for all. But in space you cannot just dump things overboard at random. Water, for example, might freeze in the tubes which are expelling it, blocking any further attempts at dumping it, and really creating a problem. Storage on board the craft was the answer, but the tanks were filling quicker than expected. Again "power down" flight was ordered and the spacecraft drifted silently, or nearly so. As each day passed, a decision was made to go on for one more day. Americans waited to see if the full mission could be completed.

They went to work, and they came home, and they ate and slept, knowing that all the time two American spacemen were drifting overhead, piling record upon record for endurance in space, and learning more and more about man and his abilities in this hostile environment. On the seventh day, the water-storage problem diminished with the end of the mission in sight, and the astronauts once again took control.

Almost exactly eight days to the hour (one hour off) Cooper and Conrad fired retros and burned down through the atmosphere to the primary landing area south of Florida. After many false starts, and much nagging trouble, the mission had been concluded as a resounding success. During their 190 hours in space, the astronauts had circled the earth 120 times. They actually saw 120 sunrises and sunsets. They traveled a total distance of 3,300,000 miles in space, and proved that man could live and work in space for the time it would take to get to the moon and back. Bearded and tired, the two astronauts were hurried away to a session of punching and probing by doctors, debriefing, and rest.

They had been weightless for eight days, and showed no ill effects from it (though they each lost about eight pounds during the flight). Earlier, another astronaut had aptly described this feeling of weightlessness.

"We might have to work out our in-flight maintenance procedures a little differently in order to keep the nuts and bolts tight during a long flight," explained Scott Carpenter, "but this perfect freedom from the restraint of gravity appealed to me as the kind of element in which I could easily belong. I was certainly right about that. The greatest thrill I had on my own flight in Aurora 7 was experiencing the state of weightlessness. I don't think anyone can imagine until he's tried it what it is like to have no feeling of up or down, to be able to spin a camera around in front of you without its falling. A change of attitude means nothing in this state. Nothing rises or falls. 'Up' loses all significance. You can assign your own 'up' and put it anywhere—towards the ground, towards the horizon or on a line between two stars—and it is perfectly satisfactory."

There was no question about it, our space effort was moving faster and faster. Gemini-Titan Six was scheduled for the latter part of October and the astronauts' names were announced.

Command pilot would be Walter M. Schirra who had piloted the near flawless "bull's-eye" Mercury-Atlas Eight flight three years before. Schirra is one of the most unrelenting competitors on the teams of astronauts, yet perhaps the most jovial and outgoing at the same time. His father had been an aerial circus flyer, his mother a wingwalker, and now he was piloting capsules in space.

Thomas P. Stafford, another astronaut from the second group, would strap into the right-hand couch in the capsule and serve as pilot. Although each astronaut becomes an expert on every part of his job, each man is also assigned an area in which he becomes a specialist. Stafford's area was communications and pre-flight check out.

Schirra and Stafford would need the perfection which Schirra had displayed on Sigma Seven, the Mercury craft, for Gemini-Titan Six was to be, primarily, America's first concentrated "space chase." The two men would attempt to "hook up" with another (unmanned) space object, the Agena stage of an Atlas-Agena missile. This maneuver would have to become completely routine before moon flights could be attempted.

The odds, according to one space official, were against success on this first try. Docking in space is an extremely critical maneuver in which every system must function perfectly.

Why were officials and safety engineers worried? After all, lift-offs had been perfected to the point where they offered little problem. Many flights in space had proven that man could survive there in relative comfort. Problems, even serious ones, had actually been solved by astronauts in space. All systems were backed-up, then the back-ups were rarely called upon. Retrograde and reentry procedures were almost perfect. Recovery was routine.

Why did they worry?

They worried about glitches and they worried, according to one safety engineer, about an old engineering premise known as "Murphy's Law."

It states: "If something can be put together or operated improperly, it eventually will be, and this will cause a failure at the most inopportune time, at the most inaccessible location."

Once, to illustrate how Murphy's Law works, a ground technician plugged two simple wires into a missile, but into the *wrong sockets,* a glaring error in view of the fact that thousands and thousands of very critical operations had gone before, and in view of the fact that he had plugged the wires into the correct sockets many times before. Fortunately, since the mistake could have cost the lives of other men, it was discovered before any damage was done.

The weather for Gemini Six was excellent. For the first time, there was very little poor weather to be found *all the way around the world.* The entire proposed flight path was clear.

On the launch pad, there was little tension. Men joked with each other, and laughed, and even the astronauts appeared carefree as they were elevated to the capsule level. Wally Schirra stepped into the "white room" which enclosed the capsule atop the rocket and grinned at technicians there. For a relaxed moment he reverted to his rank of Captain in the U.S. Navy, walking about the room wiping his finger here and there above doorways and on shelves and ledges.

Naturally he found no dust, and so he grinned broadly again and stepped to the hatch in the capsule. Tom Stafford, the only astronaut trained to be ambidextrous (to use either hand with equal dexterity) followed Schirra, and both spacesuit-clad men entered the capsule.

The Atlas-Agena rocket to which the astronauts would dock in space was being counted down about a mile away from the Gemini pad nineteen. Down on the Atlas pad, number fourteen, everything seemed to be going perfectly.

The Atlas would go first and then after a precisely calculated delay of about an hour, the Gemini-Titan with its two-man crew would blast off. This would place the two space objects in position for a later rendezvous.

If something should happen to cause a hold in one countdown, the other would also hold. If something should happen to cause a hold in the Gemini count after the Atlas had left the pad, other Gemini firing times were pre-calculated to give the astronauts the same rendezvous advantage, the Atlas merely orbiting the Earth in the meantime.

If something should happen to the Atlas in the air, after firing (a very unlikely occurrence), the remainder of the mission would be scrubbed. The Gemini would not leave the ground.

Exactly on schedule, at 10:00:04 A.M. on October 25, 1965, the Atlas blasted away on a long tongue of flame. The lift-off appeared perfect. At two minutes and twelve seconds after launch, the booster cut off on schedule. At four minutes and forty-four seconds after launch, SECO occurred (Sustainer Engine Cut-Off). Everything was going normally. The astronauts, by then strapped into their capsule and awaiting their own blast-off, watched their target on television with millions of Americans.

Then came the first hint of trouble.

"We are awaiting telemetry confirmation of Agena burn at

seven minutes and thirty seconds into the mission," said the voice from control. The target was to inject itself into orbit using its own engine and fuel. The Atlas had fallen away on schedule.

"We have had a dramatic telemetry cut-off," intoned the voice, "but we may be reading 'S' and 'C' bands (other radio bands)." Then the voice carried a definite warning. "The Canary Islands cannot 'work' Agena."

Canary was the last station until Australia which could "skin track" the Agena target. This term means to track the actual object by radar, rather than to track it by computer and telemetry data. Even if the Agena was silent, the radar should "see" it.

Technicians followed an imaginary object in the sky where the silent Agena would be if it achieved orbit. If Australia could not pick it up by radar at the right time, it was not there.

Meanwhile, control announced, "The situation is not a happy one."

America had put scores of unmanned satellites into orbit without a problem. This would be one of the worst possible ones for a glitch to strike.

But apparently a malfunction had occurred in space. On pad nineteen they stopped the count and planned to hold until word came of the success or failure of the Agena target. If the docking target had not achieved orbit, there would be no reason to go on.

Finally, the word came as the phantom spot in the sky reached the limits of the Australian tracking station, the next site with a radar capable of locating an object in space. Radar scanned space, and could find nothing. The phantom was, indeed, a phantom and nothing more. The Agena target had apparently blown up and fallen into the Atlantic Ocean the moment its engine fired.

The mission was scrubbed, and America had suffered her first major failure in the manned space program. With shoulders bent, the disappointed astronauts climbed from their capsule and took the long ride back to the ground and back to their quarters.

Schirra and Stafford would not be scheduled again until 1966.

Americans breathed a sigh of sadness, tempered with relief that the spacemen had not been aboard the missile which failed.

Later it was announced that a radar skin track had located *five* pieces in the sky where only the single Agena should have been. This information seemed to confirm the explosion in space theory. But, officials warned, it would be many days and perhaps weeks before the full reason for the failure was learned.

Immediately, though, an unusual schedule advance was announced. Since a mated Atlas-Agena was not quickly available for another try at Gemini-Titan Six, but would take many weeks to prepare, Gemini-Titan Seven would be moved forward and fired next. This way, our effort to get to the moon would not be set back.

Astronauts Frank Borman and James Lovell redoubled their preparation and training schedule with the change of dates. Both from the second group of astronauts, they were planning fourteen days in space, an all-time record, in November.

7

Americans were bitterly disappointed. Astronauts Borman and Lovell would certainly gain new knowledge on this last of the medical flights, and would prove again the possibility of extended endurance in space, but the space rendezvous had failed, and only a successful rendezvous would make things right again.

Space officials continued to plan for Gemini Seven. It would be the longest, toughest flight ever made. It would demand more from astronauts than ever before. Borman and Lovell were chosen for this mission because of their ability to withstand hardship, cramped conditions for long periods, and loneliness.

Behind the scene, however, other plans were being considered. The Gemini Six spacecraft had been counted down without a flaw. It was no fault of this capsule that the Six mission had failed. The spacecraft, after the failure of the target, had been immediately brought back down from the top of the Titan rocket and then sealed in a hangar under constant guard. It was equipped for rendezvous, and ready for rendezvous. Other Titan boosters were nearly ready for the thrust into space.

Also, astronauts Walter Schirra and Tom Stafford were primed and ready for a rendezvous attempt. The failure of the Six mission had not affected their own ability to perform. It may, in fact, have sharpened them even more. They were anxious to go.

So, in November of 1965, a dramatic announcement came from the Manned Spacecraft Center in Texas.

Gemini Seven would blast off on an endurance mission on December 3. Seven would remain in space, piloted by Frank Borman and Jim Lovell, for fourteen days, giving the United States a new record and much new evidence on space endurance.

Then, if launch pad nineteen was not damaged too severely by Seven's blast, and if a fast enough "turnaround" (installation of a new Titan with the Six capsule) could be accomplished, and if Schirra and Stafford were ready, and if the capsule and booster checked out perfectly, and if many other matters could be resolved, *Gemini Six would attempt to rendezvous with the orbiting Gemini Seven!!*

The announcement caught the fancy of Americans, and interest in the space effort redoubled. For the first time in history it was possible that *four* astronauts would be in space at the same time from the same country. It was possible that they would be in space *together,* actually flying in formation.

Warnings were quickly flashed from the Manned Spacecraft Center. Chances for the success of this mission were even less than those for the original "space chase," actually less than 50 per cent. There were too many places where the mission could be stopped before it ever started, and even if it did get away from the ground, they warned, the technical problems of rendezvous were great indeed.

But Americans were hopeful and confident. If this fantastic plan succeeded, it would be the greatest single space accomplishment since the first achievement of orbital flight. Also important to some Americans was the idea that this would surpass any Soviet accomplishment yet announced.

It was raining early in the morning on December 3, but rain, we had learned, need not cause an immediate and unqualified "scrub" of a space mission. The GT-7 rocket and spacecraft stood poised and ready, and the countdown proceeded. By early afternoon the count had reached T minus 100 minutes, and everything was "green." At T minus 50 minutes, with the count proceeding normally, all boards were still green. A critical status-control check occurred at T minus 48 minutes and 15 seconds.

"Everything is 'GO,' " was the report.

Meanwhile, astronauts Borman and Lovell had arrived at the pad and been helped into the spacecraft far up on the top of the ten-story-high rocket. They were wearing new lightweight space suits, only 16 pounds compared to the older 22-pound suits.

The reason for these new, easier-to-wear suits was announced.

During the long flight, they would remove the suits, and for the first time man would fly in space without the protection of a pressure suit. They would, however, alternate at such unprotected flying. There was always the hazard that the cabin might lose its pressure, and officials wanted at least one man to be prepared for this at all times.

At T minus 35 minutes the huge erector-framework slowly lowered and the rocket stood alone and ready. The countdown went forward perfectly. The rain had stopped and sunlight slanted down across the shining rocket.

The launch pad was cleared of all workers at T minus 28 minutes, and the count continued. Borman and Lovell waited calmly atop the rocket.

The newest "Gemini twins" completed a very critical check of all spacecraft and rocket elements at T minus 8 minutes. This check of instruments, a part of every rocket countdown, must be perfect or a hold is ordered. It was perfect. All systems were "go."

Moving to T minus 3 minutes, the count proceeded as one of the most perfect ever accomplished at the Cape. The automatic-engine-starter sequence cut in, then the voice of the ground communicator droned its familiar, dramatic final count.

". . . four . . . three . . . two . . . one . . . ignition!"

Slowly and ponderously at first, then faster and faster, the rocket thrust upward to the thunder of its engines.

"Straight as an arrow!" shouted the communicator jubilantly.

Then, "SECO (Sustainer Engine Cut-Off) at five minutes and forty seconds into the mission," came the announcement. It noted the end of the powered phase of the mission, and all was going perfectly. The thrust which had been developed would carry the spacecraft into orbit, if all continued as planned. Once again, as it had so many times before, America waited tensely for the word.

It came. "You are GO . . . you are GO!"

The launch had been successful, and the spacecraft was in orbit.

A cheerful voice came down from the hurtling capsule.

“That was the best ‘SIM’ (Simulated Lift-Off) we’ve had!” Of course this was not a simulation, but the real thing.

“You’re right down the slot!” agreed the communicator from Earth.

America’s greatest space challenge had started smoothly. Two men were in space; two more would join them if the odds could be overcome. Almost immediately workers swarmed over the still-smoking launch pad to assess the damage, to see if it could be used again without major repairs. As suspected, the searing flames of Seven had caused only minor damage. Pad nineteen (the only Gemini launch pad), with some repairs, could be made ready for the installation of another Titan within hours.

The almost impossible turnaround schedule could, at least in the beginning, be met. Everything was proceeding as planned.

Meanwhile, in space, astronauts Borman and Lovell, both from the second group, enjoyed the spectacle of space flight for the first time. For a while they flew in formation with their spent booster rocket, then they watched it drop slowly away.

“How do you like it up there?” mission control asked.

“It’s great!” answered Borman enthusiastically.

“Outstanding!” agreed Lovell.

But space flights are not made for the pure pleasure of astronauts, in spite of the enjoyment they have in space. The Gemini twins settled down to a schedule of work. It would be several days before they were joined by more astronauts, if they were joined at all.

On the ground, workers struggled to meet the demanding Gemini Six preparation schedule. In space, Borman and Lovell started their experiments. These tests ranged from something as seemingly commonplace as flying in “long-john” underwear (to test changes in an astronaut’s body without his pressure suit) to as complex a matter as talking to Earth over a laser beam (to check long-distance communication possibilities).

Eighteen other assignments were scheduled during the two-week endurance mission. They were to make a close study of blood in space, study their own alertness under extended weightlessness, study the depth of their own sleep, measure contrast between land and sea from space, make star studies, and do other scientific experiments.

The one experiment of prime importance, at least to Americans, was the upcoming rendezvous maneuver. So while the two men in space, who are perhaps the closest friends in the groups of astronauts, flew on, work proceeded on the ground.

Quickly the pad was cleared and cleaned, and minor repairs made to electrical circuits which had been burned by Seven's flames. A new Titan rocket was installed, and the Six spacecraft was bolted to its nose. The critical, highly involved, checking of circuits and systems started. Everything was proceeding according to schedule, and so the launch date was announced. If all went well, GT-6 would blast off the following Sunday, December 12, in the early morning. The lift-off would come as Borman and Lovell in GT-7 passed over the Cape so that Seven and Six would be in proper position to meet in space.

Schirra and Stafford happily prepared. Once they had waited in the spacecraft but never left the ground. This time, they hoped, things would be different.

From space Borman announced casually, "We're just getting squared away for a long winter's flight."

These early words were confirmed much later when the tired, bearded astronauts, admittedly "a little crummy from a lack of bathing" announced, "Fourteen days look a lot shorter down there than they do up here."

Early the following Sunday morning Schirra and Stafford were again installed in the cramped spacecraft on pad nineteen. As Borman and Lovell hurtled across the United States from the west, watching downward intently to catch a glimpse of the blast-off of their "space partners," the countdown progressed. It had been perfect.

Even then, space officials repeated the warning. "There is only a fifty per cent chance, at best, of success." The complex, fantastically precise maneuver of placing two spaceships side by side had never been attempted before. The comparatively simple problem of figuring orbits, for example, would have taken hundreds of mathematicians thousands of hours to work out. Banks of computers were used instead, and the "readouts" were assumed to be correct. The countdown reached zero as the men in GT-7 were passing over.

From space, command pilot Borman's disappointed words told the story.

"I saw ignition . . . and then shutdown."

Inexplicably, the huge Titan engines had fired on schedule but then had shut themselves off a second later. For tense moments, sitting atop a highly explosive mass of fuel, Schirra waited with his hand on the "D" ring in the capsule. If he pulled it, the two men would be fired away from the potentially deadly rocket but the capsule would be ruined for any further attempt at rendezvous. If he didn't pull it, and the rocket did explode, the two men would be killed.

With nerves of ice, Schirra waited.

The rocket did not explode.

But the mission, for the second time, had failed. Heartbroken, Schirra and Stafford again climbed out of the Gemini Six spacecraft as Borman and Lovell ranged on around the world far above.

The word flashed to America. A small plug at the base of the Titan had dropped free, probably due to the vibration of the engines. It should not have done so until *pulled* free by the actual lift-off (which would not have occurred for another second). Remember years back and the humorous failure of MR-1? The situation was similar, but no longer funny.

The premature release of the plug had sent a signal confirming lift-off . . . but too soon. Other circuits did not agree. Lift-off had *not* occurred. Something was wrong, said the electronic brains. So, as programmed, the automatic shutoff system had sensed the problem, and acted.

Astronaut Schirra's coolness under extreme pressure, however, had saved the capsule and made one last attempt possible. Neither the spacecraft nor the booster had been damaged by the premature shutdown, and pad nineteen was only slightly damaged by the brief burst of flame.

Another turnaround would be attempted, announced space officials. The new launch date: early morning on the following Wednesday, December 15, 1965. This would be the last chance to attempt rendezvous with GT-7 for they would soon return to Earth. If this attempt failed, no more would be made until late in the first quarter of 1966, and America would have suffered a serious setback in spite of the odds against the amazing mission in the first place.

Ironically, the odds were found to be even greater than they first seemed. Workers discovered a small "dust cap" which had been left in the propulsion system by a hurried worker. If the plug had not dropped loose too soon, the dust cap would have caused a shutdown of engines anyhow. A fine example of a space-age glitch.

As the turnaround was rushed forward, Borman and Lovell continued to pile record on record for total space-time endurance. One hundred eighty-six miles high and speeding along at *17,500 miles per hour,* they circled the Earth day after day.

They slept lightly, as other astronauts have done. The noise from astronaut Lovell's pneumatic inflation-cuffs (for systematic checking of blood pressure) bothered their sleep, as did the long total weightlessness. But they had settled into their confined life remarkably well otherwise, better than any other team of astronauts.

Once, upon hearing news of a tragic airplane crash on Earth, they commented, "Looks as if we're safer here than down there."

Another time, Borman received a message, "Condition three."

This was to inform him that his fourth child, expected momentarily, had not yet arrived.

In spite of the fact that no manned turnaround had ever been accomplished in less than six weeks, work proceeded quickly but carefully on the ground for the *second* such turnaround in *six days.* The scheduled lift-off date, the last one possible, was rapidly approaching.

The morning of December 15 dawned over the Cape in Florida, and this time America stopped almost completely. This was it. The most dramatic, most nearly impossible, space effort in history was scheduled to blast off on its final chance for success.

For the third time, astronauts Schirra and Stafford suited-up and were lifted to the white room at the capsule level of the rocket. The fuel system had been purged (cleaned) and the rocket had been refueled the night before. The dust cap had been removed and the system completely checked for other such glitches. The troublesome plug at the base of the Titan had been wired in place with breakaway wire. Everything seemed ready. Indeed, the countdown was proceeding perfectly, without a hold.

Borman and Lovell approached the Cape, high in space.

At T minus 3 minutes the first hold in the long countdown occurred . . . but this one was planned and expected, and indicated no problems. Rather, it indicated that the countdown was going so well that a built-in 25-minute hold had become necessary in order to hit the most precise lift-off time. The hold had been built into the countdown just in case of trouble; now everybody merely waited through it.

Gemini-Titan Six, with batteries instead of fuel cells for power (they wouldn't be up long enough to need the cells), far less food, and far more maneuvering fuel than GT-7, checked out perfectly during last-second systems tests. The countdown reached zero just as Borman and Lovell streaked overhead.

This time, Borman's words were jubilant as he called down, and so were the words of the communicators. For, with a thundering roar, Gemini Six rose toward space. The astronauts in Seven saw them coming up, and the communicator shouted happily, "Right down the middle!!"

The odds against success were still great, but were reducing.

One radio announcer voiced the words of everybody as Six reached upward.

"This whole nation pushed that one up," he said with a choke in his voice.

Americans wanted this one, and the astronauts were on their way to giving it.

Still, it was too soon to shout. They weren't in orbit yet, and even then great problems in rendezvous would face them. The first stage of Six dropped away smoothly and the second-stage engines fired. Altitude errors, according to pilot Stafford, were zero. Then SECO occurred precisely on the second.

Spacecraft Six, it was quickly determined, had been injected almost *perfectly.* It hurtled into an exact orbit.

"You can't do any better than that," droned astronaut Deke Slayton from the ground console.

"You are GO!" said astronaut Elliott See, the CapCom and pilot on the next Gemini mission.

"Wonderful!" drifted down a far voice. It came from astronaut Borman, now no longer alone with his partner in space. Now *four* Americans were in space, in orbit.

Exactly on the preplanned flight path, Six trailed Seven out over the Indian Ocean by 1200 miles, but lower and thus "faster" (in the respect that a racing car on the inside of the track gets around quicker than one on the outside of the track, even though speeds are the same). Gradually, Six was catching Seven.

If ever mission controllers held their breath, this was the time. Success was so near, and yet so far away. Several corrective maneuvers (or "burns") would be necessary to bring the spaceships within 2000 feet of each other, considered by space officials to signify total success in rendezvous. They were still 1200 *miles* apart, though closing on schedule.

On the ground, optimism was apparent. Colonel Richard C.

Dineen, Launch Vehicle Director, was saying, "Happiness is a successful launch." And, with Six's previous failures in mind, Gemini Program Director Charles W. Mathews said seriously, "Gemini of the past months typifies the American people. Stubbornness and stick-to-itiveness until the job is done."

Though many extremely critical burns had yet to be accomplished, the spirit of "the worst is over" prevailed on the ground. Perhaps it was because one of the most skilled of the astronauts, Walter Schirra, was at the controls. It would be his primary responsibility to bring the two craft together. There was little more the ground controllers could do. It had become, with the help of radar, a "human vision and skill" problem.

At that moment, on the ground, workers were moving onto steaming pad nineteen to begin preparations for Gemini-Titan Eight, scheduled for early in 1966.

In space, Seven continued on its near-perfect circular orbit while Six orbited in its planned *oval.* The first critical burn occurred on schedule, and Six moved into a position 600 miles behind and 74 miles below Seven at the low point in Six's orbit, only *15* miles below Seven at Six's high point.

So far, according to mission control, the flight had been "textbook perfect."

Around the world came the two spaceships to pass over the United States for the first time.

"This will be a UHF-6 pass," radioed CapCom, informing the astronauts, all four of them, that their voices would be heard live at the moment they were speaking by people all over the world.

"Be it ever so humble, there's *no* place like home," sighed Jim Lovell from Seven as the quartet passed over Texas. He and his partner had been in space, in the cramped confines of the spaceship, for many days, and they had many more days to go. Most of the astronauts with their families live near the Manned Spacecraft Center in Houston.

With infinite skill and precision, Schirra moved Six to within

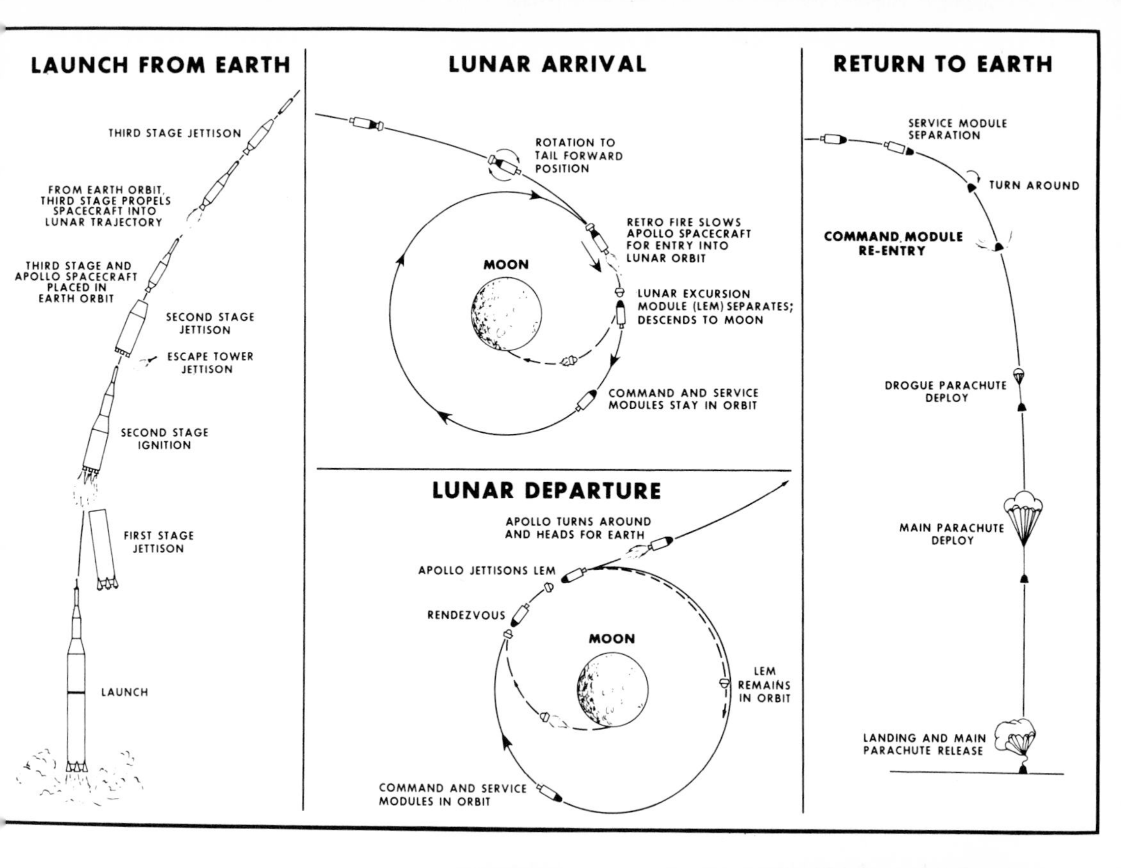

Sequence of major events in Apollo lunar exploration mission.

Mockup of Lunar Exploration Module which will actually land on the surface of the moon.

First stage cut-off and separation of moon-bound Apollo Spacemen.

In deep space the faring plates which protected the LEM drop away.

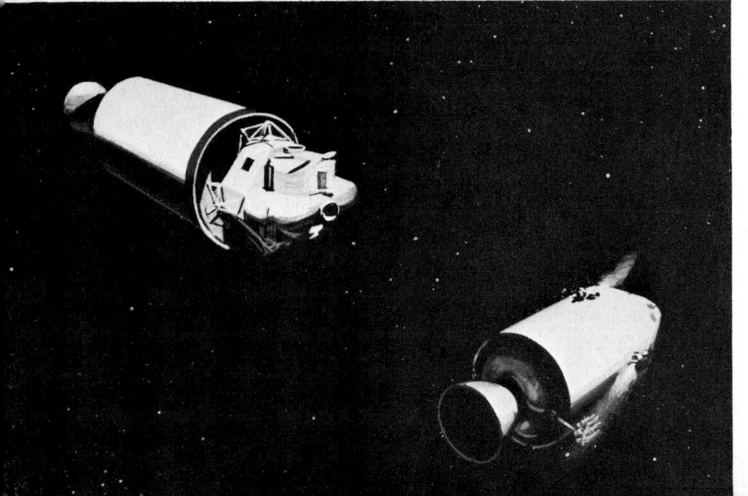

The Command and Service Modules turn end to end in deep space and dock with LEM, a critical maneuver.

Immediately following the docking, the third stage separates and drifts away.

Two spacemen transfer through a hatch into the LEM in preparation for landing on the moon. A third man remains to pilot the Command and Service Modules.

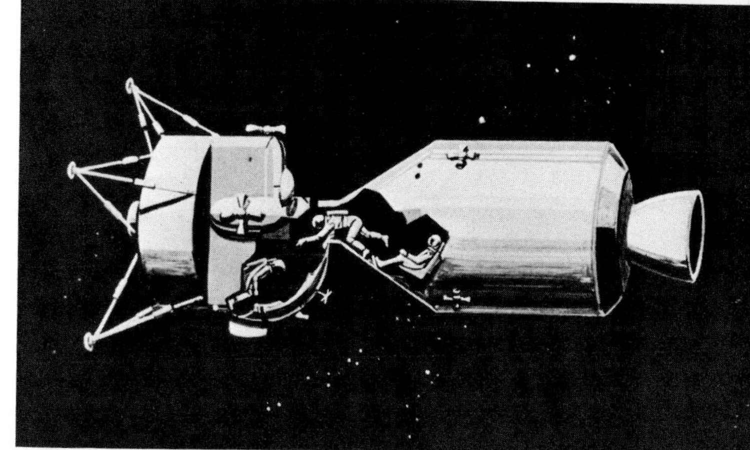

Sequence showing lunar landing of the LEM on the moon.

Spacemen will leave the LEM and explore nearby areas on the surface of the moon, leaving recording devices and bringing back samples.

The cabin of the LEM blasts away from its three-legged "launch pad."

480 miles of Seven, still below it by several miles. Although million-candlepower lights were flashing from each spaceship, no visible contact had yet been made.

By 1:45 P.M., on course, Six had moved to within 50 miles behind and 15 miles below on a circular orbit. Everybody at the Manned Spacecraft Center, and at the Cape, and across America, waited. Could it be that we were going to succeed?

The most critical "terminal maneuver" was due. Here, with a precise burn, Schirra would bring the two ships together on the same orbit.

Then came another jump toward success. The two radars had "locked on" each other. The spaceships had drawn near enough in space that the radar of each had acquired the other and was feeding data into spaceship computers to assist the rendezvous.

Happily (and for the first time in history from spaceship to spaceship) Schirra radioed, "We'll be up shortly."

The final transfer-maneuver occurred at 1:57 in the afternoon.

Two minutes later, the two ships were a mere 26 miles apart, separated by a vertical distance of slightly over 14 miles.

A garbled transmission (the two ships were approaching a zone of poor communication) came from Tom Stafford. Reminiscent of World War Two, he called, "I have him at 12 o'clock high!"

A visual sighting! The odds tumbled!

The distance closed to 20 miles apart, 13 up and down. Then 12 miles apart, 11 up and down. Then 9 apart, 5 up and down. An astounding thing was happening in space, and all America knew it. At 2:15 the ships were 4 miles apart. Six, still below, was closing but passing Seven, as planned. At 2:20, the ships were even, with only 4 miles separating them vertically.

"We're braking a little . . ." droned Schirra at 2:22 P.M.

He didn't want to overshoot. The two ships continued to drift together precisely, far out in space.

Then communications faded. No novelist ever wrote a more exciting story as men on the ground strained to hear from the men in space. But they were in a position too far from any ground station for clear communications. Radar, however, still had them in sight from the ground.

"Range, 20,000 feet," came the report from ground radar.

Six began to move slightly ahead and turning.

"Range, 18,200 . . . range, 15,000 . . ." came the readings.

At about 2:26 P.M. the voice of astronaut Stafford struggled through the static of distance. "One point seven miles . . . one point three miles . . ." Then it faded again.

Far out in space, over the Indian Ocean and crossing to the Pacific Ocean, entering the dark side of the earth, the two ships moved closer and closer.

Finally, five hours and fifty-four minutes after the thundering launch, the voice of Tom Stafford broke through. He was calm, but the world came to attention.

"We're 120 feet apart and sitting."

One hundred and twenty feet . . . far better than the 2000 feet which would have indicated total success. The astronauts could almost see each other from ship to ship.

Communications were still not good, murky and difficult to read, but Schirra repeated, "We jockeyed into position about 120 feet."

Moments later mission control, expecting that they had probably drifted apart, asked, "What's your range now?"

"About twenty feet," came the calm answer.

Then, seconds later, "We're down to ten feet."

The mission was an astounding success. Before they separated, the two ships drew to within *one foot* of each other. Docking, according to mission control, would have been "A piece of cake," or, very simple. The tough part had been conquered.

Communications improved as the ships drifted, nose to nose, across Hawaii and the United States.

"There seems to be a lot of traffic up here," drawled Schirra from spacecraft Six.

“Call a policeman,” joked Borman from Seven.

“You’re up close,” informed Shirra.

From Seven, Lovell replied, “I can see your lips moving.”

“I’m chewing gum,” said Schirra.

“Oh, OK,” answered Lovell from Seven. “Can you see Frank’s beard, Wally?” (This was in reference to the fact that Seven’s astronauts had been up without shaving for twelve days when the rendezvous occurred.)

“Yeah, I can see yours too.”

For the first time in history, a spaceman in one ship inspected the ship of another spaceman.

“You guys are really a shoddy-looking group with all those wires hanging around,” Schirra announced after the inspection of Seven.

He was referring to wires left after the sustainer engine had dropped away from Seven nearly two weeks earlier. But Six had trailing wires, too, and Borman quickly informed Schirra of this.

After being told where the wires were trailing from, Borman shot back, “That’s exactly where you’ve got one too. It really was snapping around there when you were firing your thrusters. Looks like about eight or nine feet long, and double wire.”

“Right,” from Six.

“Wait till I take a picture of it,” asked Borman.

Over Africa, Six worried about Seven’s food supply.

“Oh, we’re in good shape,” came the answer from Seven. “It’s holding out, but it’s the same thing from day to day.”

Then, to the ground, Borman happily announced, “We have company tonight.”

On the night side of the Earth again, Schirra commented to Lovell, “Those forest fires really stick out, don’t they?” The fires were on the island of Madagascar.

“Roger,” answered Lovell from Seven, which was alongside him. “You can see them all the time, Wally. That fire down there to your left is an oil fire, I think.”

"Well, I'll be darned," answered Schirra.

The spacemen continued to peer through each other's windows. At one point Borman, an Air Force man, held up a hand-lettered sign to Schirra, a Navy Captain.

It read BEAT NAVY.

During this extended repartee, astronaut Stafford was taking an astonishing roll of motion-picture film showing the spaceships maneuvering about each other. Both ships accomplished preplanned maneuvering, and before they separated each of the four astronauts took a turn at formation flying in space. After seven hours, they drew apart by a distance of about twenty miles for the sleeping period.

The tracking ship *Rose Knot,* far below, called, "Have a good night's sleep. I feel like a baby-sitter. I tuck you in every night and now I'm baby-sitting for *four* of you."

Borman's answer was lost in static, but *Rose Knot* replied with deep feeling, "We're watching over you."

A final, partly garbled call came down as Schirra jokingly broke the mood. "Bluebeard, you don't have much of a mustache," he told Seven.

In the morning the two ships pulled farther apart. Six was scheduled to reenter, with Seven continuing on its amazing endurance run. Already the two astronauts in Seven had spent more combined hours in space than a *combined total* of all other space flights, both American and Soviet.

At 29:09 past 10 A.M., December 16, 1965, Gemini Six splashed down after burning through the atmosphere for the most perfect recovery in the Gemini program (though Seven made a bet with Six that they could do even better). Six landed a mere twelve miles off the bow of the prime recovery aircraft carrier *Wasp.* Schirra and Stafford were quickly brought aboard. They were smiling and dapper as they stepped out of their spacecraft on the flight deck. Gemini Seven sped on through space.

On Friday, December 17, Seven's crew was informed that the

marvelous pictures taken of them in space were being shown to television audiences around the world.

"And here we are in our underwear," was the laconic reply.

Doubtless excited at the prospect of their own recovery, particularly in view of certain problems developing in the fuel cells of their spaceship, they were looking forward to the next morning, Saturday, after fourteen long days in space.

With only nine orbits to go, Frank Borman commented, "Jim is beginning to look like Santa Claus." Christmas, 1965, was near.

Only one action remained to complete a space flight which had carried American astronauts further than they would go on a trip to the moon and back—recovery. Two spacemen had already returned safely from the rendezvous. To be a total success, the last two had to be brought safely home.

On December 18, 1965, high over the Pacific Ocean and after 329 hours and 41 minutes in space, command pilot Borman pushed the retro-fire button and the retro-sequence started.

"Are you ready to come home?" asked the ground.

"Ready . . . ready," they answered enthusiastically.

At 8:30 A.M., a perfect retro-fire sequence was confirmed by ground telemetry equipment. Seven was starting its long blistering plunge through the atmosphere. In the recovery area in the Atlantic Ocean, the aircraft carrier *Wasp* waited.

Over Hawaii, the last station before the United States, the call flashed up to the two astronauts in the falling spacecraft. "As you come up to my LOS (loss of signal), you're looking real good. We'll see you."

Down across the United States they burned, heading directly for their small "footprint" recovery area. For long moments they were in the expected ionization-blackout zone, and were not heard from. But ground equipment continued to indicate that all was going well.

Finally the call came from Borman. "Main chute out and looks OK."

At 5 minutes and 40 seconds after 9 A.M., precisely on schedule and, as Gemini Six, within twelve miles of the *Wasp,* Seven splashed down. They had been in space a total of 330 hours, 35 minutes and 13 seconds. They had traveled more than *five and one-half million* miles in the past fourteen days. They had accomplished every major task of the amazing mission.

Upon landing, Borman spoke for both of them, saying, "We're glad to be here . . . you don't know how glad."

A new phrase was coined for the joint missions of Six and Seven—"The Spirit of 76."

Although Frank Borman jokingly complained, "Gemini is a beautiful spacecraft, but a lousy boat," both men checked out in fine health after their ordeal.

In spite of their long confinement in a cramped space, they walked steadily across the flight deck of the *Wasp,* smiling broadly all the time.

The accomplishments of "76"? For the first time in history spaceships had rendezvoused. The fastest "turnaround" in space history. Four men in space at the same time for the first time in history. A new, almost unbeatable, endurance record in space. Formation flying for the first time in space. And volumes of extremely valuable medical information about space flight.

In January of 1966, the first (unmanned) Apollo flight was scheduled. The distance to the moon seemed suddenly shorter.

8

"I must take this time to say a little prayer for all the people, including myself, who are involved in this operation. I want to thank You especially for letting me fly this flight. Thank You for the privilege of being able to be in this position, to be in this wondrous place, seeing all these startling wonderful things that You have created.

"Help guide and direct all of us that we may shape our lives to be much better Christians. So that we help one another and work with one another rather than fighting and bickering. Help us to complete this mission successfully.

"Help us in future space endeavors to show the world that democracy really can compete and still is able to do things in a big way. And are able to do research, development, and conduct new scientific and technical programs.

"Be with all our families. Give us guidance and encouragement and let them know that everything will be OK. We ask in Thy name.

"Amen."

These words came from a man in space, in a spacecraft traveling at over 17,000 miles per hour, and have become the astronauts' prayer. They were said by Gordon Cooper during the sixteenth orbit of his record-making 22-orbit Mercury mission on May 16, 1963.

They will be repeated by others as we probe deeper and deeper into space, farther and farther from our own planet.

In spite of the initial failure of Gemini-Titan Six, the program is progressing satisfactorily. Soon the Gemini schedule will call for a flight of great drama. Astronaut Neil Armstrong will fly a capsule while astronaut David Scott crawls out the hatch and, untethered to the craft, drifts *completely around the world.*

This magnificent adventure is planned for 1966.

And what then?

The moon project!

Whether Scott's long walk in space and the docking flight of Schirra and Stafford ends the Gemini project, or whether more are scheduled to gain further knowledge and to perfect techniques, the next step in space will be perhaps the most thrilling of all.

Project Apollo!

This is the project which will eventually put three men in space, and two of them on the surface of the moon. Plans call for the first manned Apollo shot from Merritt Island in 1967. Using the gigantic Saturn V rocket, 360 feet tall and developing a thrust of 7,500,000 pounds (the Redstone, remember, developed only 82,000 pounds and was only 80 feet tall), men will first orbit the Earth in flights as far out as 22,300 miles for periods ranging from fourteen days to *forty-five* days. If a supply ship has been developed in the meantime, these times will be extended to three months or more in space.

Then men will orbit the moon on flights up to twenty-eight days during which the three-man crew will survey the surface of our nearest neighbor in space.

Finally, man will land on the moon.

Let's follow this first moon mission. Before we follow it, though, let's check on what might have happened in the meantime, before this first manned lunar flight.

We will surely have landed many experimental devices on the surface of the moon, using what is called the "soft-landing" technique. These will include whole and operating television cameras, measuring instruments, and even bacteriological devices. Twenty-five such lunar-surface exploration devices are planned before man first sets off on his journey.

He will know, before he goes, what to expect when he gets there.

Very possibly we will have soft-landed an entire experimental laboratory which will wait, silent and dead, until activated by the first men on the moon.

Another docking maneuver as the LEM cabin rejoins the Command and Service Modules which have been orbiting the moon.

After cutting the LEM loose and returning near Earth, the Service Module breaks away, leaving only the Command Module to re-enter.

Tiny compared to what it was when the whole unit blasted away from Earth, the Command Module is gently lowered on three huge parachutes to waiting recovery forces.

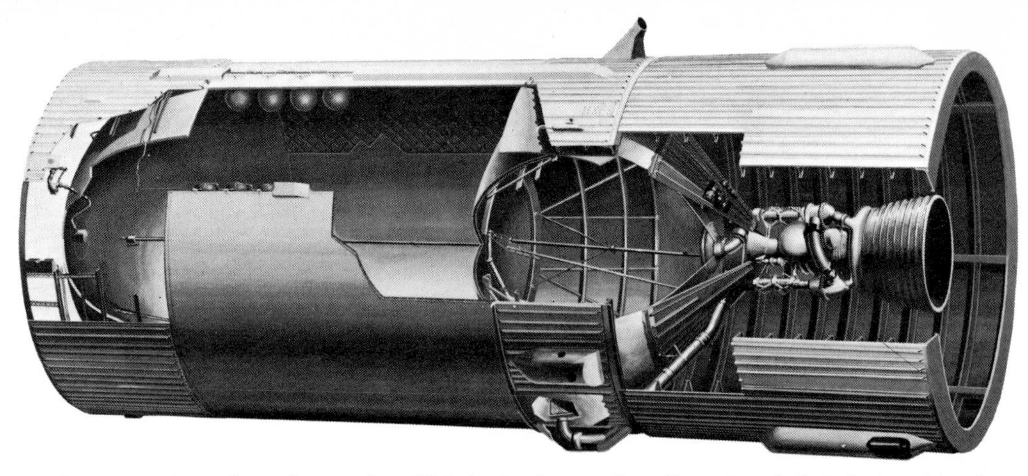

Cut-away view of a rocket engine. This is the Saturn Four-B engine. Left is fuel tank and right is engine nozzle.

Space Truck Readied—The lunar Saturn Five's second-stage five engines dwarf technicians preparing "battleship" vehicle for hot firing at North American Space Division's Santa Susana (Calif.) static test lab. Battleship test vehicle, which contains five hydrogen-powered Rocketdyne-built J-2 engines, is similar to the 82-foot-long Saturn S-11 second stage that will help send astronauts to the moon.

A lunar mobile laboratory under development at Grummon Aircraft. It will carry men and equipment, and will travel about the moon. Powered by electric motors, the unit can pull as many trailers as needed.

Another proposed Lunar Exploration Vehicle.

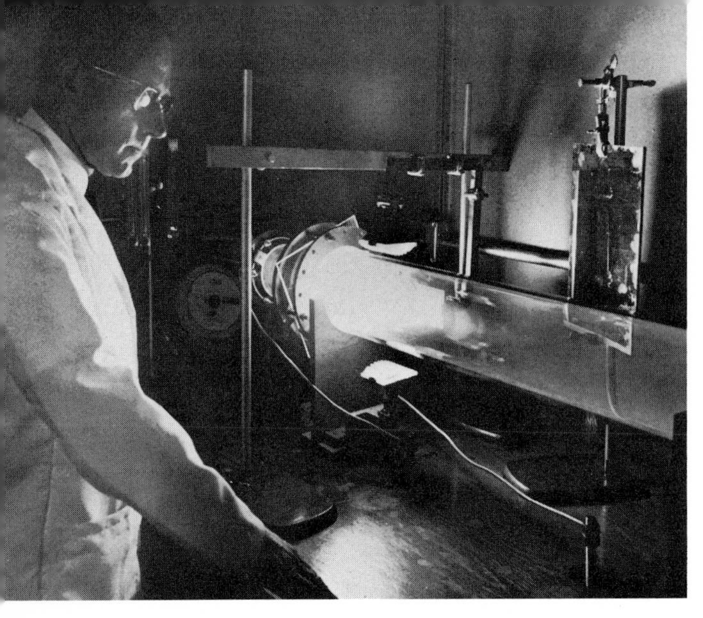

Tests are being conducted at Lockheed with plasma, the gas which comprises more than 99 per cent of the universe. A new form of power may be developed which will help man reach the stars.

Life on the Moon—Resembling a cartwheel, this underground life center is made of booster tanks arranged in a cluster connecting living quarters, medical center, recreation areas, shop facilities and personnel services. Studies now under way at North American Aviation's Space and Information Systems Division, Downey, Calif., indicated that lack of atmosphere and extreme temperatures require that man establish initial housing and operational facilities under lunar surface.

We may have space stations orbiting around Earth, manned at all times and supplied by spacecraft from Earth. Certainly we will have such stations eventually, for they will be very necessary when we send spaceships on beyond the moon to the planets.

Finally the day arrives. The morning is crisp and cool at Merritt Island, the sky dark but clear. Stars shine brightly, but at that particular time in the morning the moon is not visible.

It is April 9, 1969, a day which will be remembered in history as one of the most important to man.

Three astronauts, suited up in their silver space garb, arrive at the pad and step from the van one by one. They are relaxed, unworried, almost jovial. For a moment they stand and stare up at their monster vehicle. It is an awesome sight.

"They'll never get it off the ground," one astronaut jokes.

The two others, one a highly skilled scientist, grin at the first. It doesn't seem possible, they nod in agreement, though they have, of course, seen this great booster rise many times before.

Saturn V stands serene in the glaring light from arc lamps which bathe the area. Exhaust ports on its side constantly emit heavy white steam. Far, far above, at the very top, the Apollo Command and Service Modules rest, and hidden behind adaptor plates, just beneath these units, is the Apollo Lunar Excursion Module. This is a spidery mechanism with spindly legs designed for service and not beauty.

Streamlining, designers knew, would have little effect or use on the moon, with its total lack of atmosphere.

An elevator carries the three astronauts, and a few technicians, to the Command Module Level. They enter the module.

It is cramped, but much larger and more comfortable than the early space vehicles. An entire Mercury capsule would easily fit inside. Three form-fitting couches fill much of the space, and the rest is packed with a great variety of highly sophisticated instrumentation. But there is room, temporarily, for the technicians who help the three astronauts strap themselves in and plug their suits to the life-support mechanisms in the module. As the countdown continues, the radios and other instruments are checked for the last time.

These men have been through this before, but always as a drill and nothing more. This, however, is no drill. This time when the countdown reaches zero, the flight director will not cut things off and congratulate the men for another perfect test. This time when the count reaches zero they will lift off into space.

Dawn streaks the sky to the east and the arc lights seem to dim as the light of the sun penetrates to the pad far below.

Everything is "Go" inside. The technicians, with final slaps on the shoulders and words of encouragement, leave the module. The hatch is sealed.

The countdown continues.

Momentarily a silence settles among the men in the module. It is not, however, a silence of fear, for they are confident of the outcome of their mission, but it is rather a silence of prayer and reflection upon their own good fortune at being chosen for this great mission.

There are no holds, as with the pioneering space flights. Men and machines have been perfected, and except for an occasional glitch, holds are a thing of the past.

". . . five . . . four . . . three . . . two . . . one . . . zero . . . ignition!

"Lift-off!"

As the words of the flight director ring in their ears, they feel the tremendous thrust of 7,500,000 pounds far below. The module trembles very slightly, and a feeling of motion is apparent. Quickly, as the speed builds, they are pushed into their couches by the great acceleration.

"Everything is 'Go'," intones the module communicator to the ground. All instruments check as they should.

His voice does not betray the excitement he cannot help feeling in his heart. Space flights may have become routine, but this one is not. This one is a first, and people know it. Countless thousands of technicians and workers have planned and built the vehicle and equipment, and the astronauts themselves have spent many months training for this moment. Millions of Americans are watching carefully. Even at that moment, a television camera in the module is scanning them.

"First-stage cutoff and separation confirmed," announces the module command pilot. On the ground they are aware of this through their own instruments, but such phases of the flight are always confirmed from space. Far below, the giant lower section of the Saturn tumbles away and down. Instantly the second stage fires and a long tongue of flame shoots backward.

The unit then begins a gradual turn to horizontal and, at about one hundred miles altitude, the second stage burns out and falls away. The Saturn is considerably smaller now as the third stage fires only briefly, then cuts off.

It is more comfortable in the module. Although the speed is still increasing, the effects of the G-forces are not so noticeable. Then, suddenly, they are not noticeable at all as the spacecraft falls into a "parking orbit" and becomes completely weightless.

In orbit all systems are once again checked carefully. Everything is still "GO." One of the crucial moments has arrived. Checked and re-checked by computer, the precise instant the third stage will once again ignite is critical. The re-ignition will speed the unit to over 25,000 miles per hour, escape velocity.

"Third stage ignition confirmed," drones the astronaut from space. The other two spacemen are busy watching instruments and checking on-board systems. Again, all three men feel the surge of power push them into their seats as the rocket accelerates.

They are leaving Earth.

In the hours to follow, several critical maneuvers will be necessary. The first and perhaps the least critical is coming up. On command, the adaptor cover plates separate and fall away, exposing the Lunar Excursion Module just beneath the Service Module. There in deep space, these faring plates are no longer necessary to protect the LEM, and preparations must be started for its use.

Coming soon after this is a very critical maneuver. Carefully, with a very light touch, the command pilot operates his control stick as the vehicle *breaks apart* between the Service Module and the LEM with its third-stage booster. Turning end for end in space, the pilot gently nudges the front half up to the rear half, docking directly into the LEM unit. Immediately the third stage is separated from the rear to drift off forever in space.

Now the spacecraft is tiny compared to what it was when it left Earth. Having turned about in space, the forward end of the unit now exposes an engine which was once concealed between the Service Module and the LEM unit.

Everything which has been learned in the past helps on this mission. The Gemini twins perfected the highly critical docking maneuver which has just occurred. Both Mercury and Gemini told man how to live in weightless space. On previous Apollo missions, thousands of hours have been spent practicing eating, drinking, and waste disposal.

A minute course correction is accomplished by using small rockets, and this assures the crew that they will speed directly to the moon. Finally, after many hours and at a most precise instant, the nose rocket of the Apollo unit fires. This slows it just enough to cause it to fall into a lunar orbit. If it is too slow, the unit will crash into the moon. If it is not slow enough, the three men will sail on into deep space, eventually perhaps falling into a *solar* orbit.

The speed is exact, and the three astronauts are orbiting the moon but not for the first time in history. This moon-orbit flight has been accomplished several times before, by several different astronauts, in preparation for what is to come next.

Two of the astronauts, a pilot and a scientist, crawl from the Apollo Command Module through a tube into the LEM unit. The third astronaut stays in the Command Module to pilot it during the next phase of the mission to the moon.

On command, the LEM unit separates from the Command Module, descending to the surface of the moon. Meanwhile, the Command Module continues on its lunar orbit, under the guidance of the pilot who remained behind.

Parachutes would be useless as the LEM unit falls to the surface. There is no atmosphere on the moon to fill a parachute and soften a landing, so the landing must be slowed to a stop by firing a rocket which spits a stream of flame *downward*, in the direction of the fall.

Imperceptibly the speed of the falling LEM decreases until, in a boiling cloud of smoke and possibly moon dust, the unit settles on the surface. Its spindly legs hold, and the rocket engine dies. The engine will have no further use, although the lower unit of the LEM will soon double as a launch pad. In the small upper cabin, the two astronauts prepare themselves for a quick trip outside. They will need cameras, equipment to remove rock samples and, of course, life-support gear.

The first manned visit to the moon's surface will, according to NASA officials, be a fast one. Astronauts will spend very little time outside their craft. But they will leave behind an automated instrument package containing seismometers, scintillometers, magnetometers, and other devices which will telemeter back to Earth continuous measurements.

So the two astronauts step through the hatch, down a ladder which has extended down one leg of the LEM unit, and onto the surface of the moon. They are jubilant. For many, many centuries, from when man first appeared on the Earth, he has looked up into the night sky at the shining moon and wondered about it. Only recently has he actually dreamed of standing on its surface.

Now they have done it, the first men to do so. They stare about in fascination, at first unable to grasp the full impact of their adventure. But they are trained and skilled men, and so they settle down to work. "It is good," one comments, "to feel gravity again . . . even if it is only one-sixth that of Earth." The other, almost to prove what his companion has said, grins and then jumps into the air, unable to resist the urge to test this new mild gravity. As he had imagined, he sails exactly six times higher than he would have on Earth. The other astronaut, meanwhile, is carrying the instrument package to a spot near a sheltered cleft in the rock surface. On Earth the package weighed several hundred pounds. Here, he lifts it with ease.

But he pauses with a startled look on his face.

There, near the cleft he had chosen for the instrument package, is a scattering of gleaming instruments and lenses. On one of the larger pieces of stainless steel, he can see the American flag, still a beautiful red, white, and blue. He knows what the device is, though he had not really expected to stumble onto one on that first visit. Later, of course, after more thorough exploration of the moon, many such devices would be found. This one he has located is one of the early Explorer probes sent to the moon by the United States. Before it crashed, it sent back many valuable photographs. Since the moon has no atmosphere, the pieces remained in shiny new condition, though it long since destroyed itself in a hard landing. He steps over some of the pieces almost reverently, then places the instrument package in position. Then he flips the switches on, checking gauges to make sure the solar batteries are operating.

His headsets suddenly snap with a voice.

"LEM, this is Command . . . everything OK down there?"

The pilot in the orbiting Module is just checking.

"Roger, all OK," answers one of the men on the moon.

Another voice comes through with much less volume.

"LEM, this is Earth CapCom . . . you have two more minutes. Acknowledge, please."

"Roger, CapCom, understand two minutes."

Chipping at a rock with a geologist's hammer provides one astronaut with samples for later study while the other snaps photos of his partner and the lunar surface. Then the two men nod.

"Ready . . .?" asks one.

"Let's go," comes the answer.

They climb back up the ladder into the upper section of the LEM unit and then seal the hatch. Soon a critical countdown comes from Earth.

". . . four . . . three . . . two . . . one . . . ignite!"

They feel the unit shudder and start up. Beneath them the bottom half of the unit remains, odd looking now and lonely. But not for long. Other men will return, and find other uses for the strange framework which came so far through space to do its job.

The rest of the journey will be near routine, except for one very critical maneuver. They must still rejoin the Command Module which is orbiting above. Falling finally into an orbit of their own, they look out the hatch window.

And they breathe a sigh of thanks for the perfection of computers. There, nearly touching them, is the Command Module in precisely the same orbit. The pilot again moves the control stick, inching the Command Module ahead, around, and gently bumping it against the hatch of LEM. The men inside hear the sealing latches snap into place.

Opening the hatch between the units, they crawl back into the cabin from which they started the long journey. The three men smile and congratulate each other. The worst is over.

Again the spacecraft is turned so that the nose of the Command Module is forward into the LEM unit. For a moment the pilot stares at the LEM, then, almost regretfully, he pushes a button and the little moon cabin breaks away for the last time to fall into a forgotten lunar orbit until it eventually crashes back to the moon many days later.

Now the spacecraft has diminished in size to one Command Module and one Service Module, small indeed compared to the giant it was when it started. A rocket engine in the Service Module fires exactly on schedule, driving the little craft out of its lunar orbit and into a long fall toward Earth. It will move faster and faster as Earth's gravity becomes stronger.

In mid-course the trajectory is corrected by firing tiny rockets in the nose of the Command Module, then the Service Module drops away to fall into still another forgotten orbit in space, or to burn to a cinder in the atmosphere of Earth which seems to be growing larger and larger as they approach. Only the small Command Module now remains, shaped very much like an original Mercury capsule only much larger.

As Apollo approaches Earth, it turns to expose its blunt-end heat shield, and the long blistering fall through the atmosphere begins. Hotter and hotter grows the heat shield, but the astronauts strapped into their couches inside are cool and comfortable. A drogue chute pops out, reminiscent of Al Shepard's flight so long ago, and then main chutes follow.

This time there are three tremendous parachutes. One could not do the job for such a heavy unit. Gently the module drops into the ocean, where recovery ships are waiting.

The first trip to the moon is completed.

On the main recovery ship, the three "moon-men" will undergo extensive physical and mental examinations to determine whether their flight, and their exposure to actual moon conditions, had any effect on them. No ill effects are found, though the spacemen seem quite exuberant about their successful mission.

Well they should be.

Back to the Cape they are flown, back to the starting point of their long flight, and they are welcomed as heroes. People line the streets of Cocoa Beach to watch them as they arrive. Men and women cheer, and the astronauts wave and smile. But when they are called upon to speak, they do as every astronaut before them has done. They credit many, many other people for their successful ride, taking very little of the credit for themselves.

The moon flights will continue for an extended period, but remain in the scientific phase. Limited travel on the moon, increasing the distance a man will move from his ship, will be followed by more extended stays. First a man will stay for a day, then two days, then one week. Later, he will stay for a month or more. He will have built shelters for himself, where he can remove his cumbersome space clothing and live in relative comfort. Finally, the establishment of a permanent scientific moon station will be completed, where a staff of men and women will live and work for long periods, supplied by rockets from Earth.

Meanwhile, scientists on Earth will not have stopped their planning and building. One day a new flight will be announced.

This one will carry man beyond the moon, to the planets.

Today, in fact, these long lonely flights are in the preliminary planning stages.

Fly-by missions with three-man crews to Venus are planned, with a target date as early as 1975. By 1979, American space scientists plan to send a mission to Mars, where three men will fly past the red planet and study it more closely than ever before possible. The Venus flight will take one year in space and scientists figure it will take two years of flying to get a crew to Mars, around this planet, and back to Earth. This length of time is required by the tricky around-Venus maneuvers necessary to reach Mars the most efficient way.

These are not idle pipe dreams.

Nor is the plan to *land a man on Mars* by *1980.* The date is much nearer than it would seem at first glance.

The landing missions will require a high-energy nuclear-powered launch vehicle, and will be flown by crews of up to eight or nine astronauts. Three will eventually descend to the surface of Mars or Venus in what is called, in the case of Mars, a MEM (Mars Excursion Module) or of Venus, a VEM. Later flights will carry twelve to eighteen astronauts, with six of them landing on the surface.

Here's an example of one of the earlier flights, a Mars fly-by.

The spacecraft will be a ten-foot diameter cylinder, about sixty feet long, and a Saturn S-2 stage earth escape booster. This latter unit will have been assembled and fueled *in earth orbit,* using multiple Saturn V launches to do the job. Saturn V, the rocket used to send the first Americans to the moon, will be used to ferry fuel and supplies to a point in space. This is another example of the "building block" technique used by space technologists, in which a rocket is at first tested, then used in a major effort, then reused in support efforts as newer and larger vehicles are introduced.

Spaceship power will be provided by radioisotope thermal generators. It is calculated that this first fly-by will carry about 10,000 pounds of scientific instrumentation, including surface and atmospheric probes that will be ejected during the actual passing of the planet, and television and motion-picture cameras. Still cameras will also be carried by the crewmen.

As the craft passes the planet at a calculated altitude of about 600 miles, the crew will toss out the scientific probes through an air-lock, and then busy themselves photographing the surface below with television, motion-picture, and still cameras. These photos, or at least the best ones, would be transmitted back to Earth as soon as possible.

The crew would reenter the Earth's atmosphere in a modified Apollo Command Module, which would use a Service Module for braking purposes. This vehicle must reduce its speed drastically, actually from hyperbolic to parabolic velocity, before hitting the atmosphere.

During the flight there and back (around Venus either going or coming) the crew would live in a relatively comfortable eighteen-foot spherical cabin at one end of the cylinder. In this cabin would be a centrifuge so that the crew, accustomed to the gravity of Earth, could exercise . . . or perhaps the whole ship will be whirled in space to produce artificial gravity. They will grow a portion of their food right in the spacecraft, and will reconstitute all waste so that everything may be used again and again. Moisture in the cabin atmosphere, for example, will be distilled and used for drinking and equipment cooling rather than being wasted. Although perhaps not pleasant to consider (but perfectly sanitary and healthful) even body wastes will be distilled and purified, and then used again. The same is true with waste foods, or garbage.

Exercise will be critically important. Away from the pull of Earth's gravity, the body of a human does not function in the same way. The heart does less work and so blood vessels and muscles lose their "tone." The bones, no longer required to meet the work of carrying the full weight of the body, lose calcium. Exercise, with or without an artificial gravity, would minimize these problems on a long flight in space.

Astronauts will probably live according to a fairly rigid plan, with certain times devoted to work, other periods for sleep, and others for recreation. Test groups have already proven that such a scheduling of time is necessary for good mental health during long periods of relative isolation, and during periods where there is no day or night.

Finally, after several fly-by missions of Mars and Venus, a part of the crew will descend to the surface of these planets in an excursion module. They will take samples for later analysis, they will photograph, and they will explore, much as the "moon men" did so many years before them. But by then, of course, there will be colonists on the moon watching these activities by television.

Will that, finally, be the end?

Not at all. For during the initial phases of planetary exploration, scientists will be studying ways to rocket men beyond the planets. We now know that many planets similar to our own exist within our own galaxy (about 64,000,000 according to one expert). Beyond our Milky Way Galaxy, many *billions* more exist. These, in fact, are only the relatively small number of planets in space which are similar to Earth. There are billions and billions more unlike Earth. Some are far too hot, perhaps, like Mercury, or bitter cold, as we imagine Pluto to be. There is no reason to imagine that life does not exist on hundreds, even thousands, of these other planets similar to our own.

Some people, in fact, feel that the existence of life on other planets beyond our own system has been *proven* . . . although earlier Mariner flights which photographed Mars and studied Venus would seem to disprove the theory of life on these particular nearby worlds. It is, however, difficult to ignore the "proof" these believers offer.

Radio sounds from outer space, regular and repetitious, convince some people. "Flying saucers," which many people feel are visitors from space, and which have been sighted with regularity (according to historical records) for hundreds of years, convince others. These sightings seem to have increased in recent years.

Discoveries which cannot otherwise be explained lead many people to believe that life similar to our own exists far beyond our own system, and that such beings have visited our planet from time to time through our own relatively short history. These examples include the discovery of a perfect cube of meteorite iron and nickel, about three inches by two inches, found embedded in a block of coal cut out of a tertiary coal bed in Lower Austria in 1877. Still on display in the Salzburg Museum, the cube is hard as steel, symmetrically shaped, and *has a geometrically-contrived groove running around it.* Reliable tests prove that the cube was placed in the coal bed at least 300,000 years ago . . . that is, 273,000 years *earlier* than man was able to perform the simplest functions. Where did the cube come from?

Or, perhaps more astounding, is the finding of a gold thread embedded in the stone of a quarry in England. By dating the rock formation, scientists were able to state that the thread was 60,000,000 years old, or, that it had been crafted by hand or machine about 59,000,000 years *before man appeared on Earth.*

There are other discoveries which defy explanation, and which coupled with the reports of unidentified flying objects and radio signals, have led many people, including a large number of highly-qualified scientists, to believe that life does exist in space. These discoveries, then, are cited as proof of the theory that there have been visitations from outer space.

According to these theories, these unexplained articles are

similar to those which our astronauts will leave here and there as they visit other worlds.

Let us, for just a moment, allow our imaginations to wander completely free.

First, imagine the almost impossible-to-imagine vastness of space, where time and distance mean nothing. Now imagine one of our own astronauts during this century leaving Earth for a first trip beyond our own solar system. Naturally a new source of rocket power has been perfected so that he can travel at the speed of light, or faster.

We cheer him on his way and then watch and listen as he journeys through space. He lands on a planet similar to our own but his orders call for no contact between himself and any creatures who might live there. He sees no living thing. He takes samples, returns to his craft, and starts his long journey back home.

But while he was there, he inadvertently dropped a nylon coated silver thread from his space suit.

A brief (in space terms) period of time passes, perhaps a million years or so. The geology of the planet has shifted, closing over the thread and locking it in. But then, at that distant time a million years from now, a workman is digging and he uncovers the thread.

Such a thread, according to the scientists of that world, could not possibly have come from there. When it was placed where the workman discovered it, determined to be that million or so years ago, their own civilization had no idea how to fashion nylon or silver.

And there you have the same thing that could have happened on our planet . . . and could be happening even today.

MANNED ORBITAL FLIGHTS OF THE UNITED STATES AND RUSSIA

Date	*Astronaut and Nation*	*Craft Name*	*Craft Weight*	*Rocket Thrust (lbs.)*	*Orbits*	*Hours & Minutes*
April 12, 61	Gagarin (USSR)	Vostok I	10,418	800,000	1	1 48
May 5, 61	Shepard (US)	Freedom 7	3000	82,000	Sub	0 15
July 21, 61	Grissom (US)	Liberty Bell 7	3000	82,000	Sub	0 15
Aug. 6–7, 61	Titov (USSR)	Vostok II	10,430	800,000	17.5	25 11
Feb. 20, 62	Glenn (US)	Friendship 7	4265	360,000	3	4 55
May 24, 62	Carpenter (US)	Aurora 7	4244	360,000	3	4 56
Aug. 11–15, 62	Nikolayev (USSR)	Vostok III	10,430	800,000	64	94 25
Aug. 12–15, 62	Popovich (USSR)	Vostok IV	10,430	800,000	48	70 57
Oct. 3, 62	Schirra (US)	Sigma 7	4325	360,000	6	9 13
May 15–16, 63	Cooper (US)	Faith 7	4000	360,000	22	34 20
June 14–19, 63	Bykovsky (USSR)	Vostok V	10,430	800,000	81	119 6
June 16–19, 63	Tereshkova	Vostok VI	10,440	800,000	48	70 50
Oct. 12–13, 64	Feoktistov & Komarov (USSR) Yegorov (USSR)	Voskhod I	16,000	900,000	16	24 17
Mar. 18–19, 65	Belyayev & Leonov (USSR)	Voskhod II	16,000	900,000	17	26 2
Mar. 23, 65	Grissom & Young (US)	Gemini 3	7,100	430,000	3	4 53
June 3–7, 65	McDivitt & White (US)	Gemini 4	7,800	530,000	62	97 48
Aug. 21–29, 65	Cooper & Conrad (US)	Gemini 5	7,000	530,000	100	190 56
Dec. 4–18, 65	Borman & Lovell (US)	Gemini 7	8,069	533,000	206	330 35
Dec. 15–16, 65	Schirra & Stafford (US)	Gemini 6	7,000	530,000	17	25 51

Russian craft weights and rocket thrusts are unofficial but estimated from Soviet press and radio reports.

AMERICAN ASTRONAUTS

First group selected

M. Scott Carpenter	U.S. Navy
L. Gordon Cooper, Jr.	U.S. Air Force
John H. Glenn, Jr.	U.S. Marine Corps
Virgil I. "Gus" Grissom	U.S. Air Force
Walter M. Schirra, Jr.	U.S. Navy
Alan B. Shepard, Jr.	U.S. Navy
Donald K. Slayton	Civilian

Second group selected

Neil A. Armstrong	Civilian
Frank Borman	U.S. Air Force
Charles Conrad, Jr.	U.S. Navy
James A. Lovell, Jr.	U.S. Navy
James A. McDivitt	U.S. Air Force
Elliot M. See, Jr.**	Civilian
Thomas P. Stafford	U.S. Air Force
Edward H. White	U.S. Air Force
John W. Young	U.S. Navy

Third group selected

Edwin E. Aldrin, Jr.	U.S. Air Force
William A. Anders	U.S. Air Force
Charles A. Bassett, II**	U.S. Air Force
Alan L. Bean	U.S. Navy
Eugene A. Cernan	U.S. Navy
Roger B. Chaffee	U.S. Navy
Michael Collins	U.S. Air Force
R. Walter Cunningham	Civilian
Donn F. Eisele	U.S. Air Force
Theodore C. Freeman**	U.S. Air Force
Richard F. Gordon, Jr.	U.S. Navy
Russell L. Schweickart	Civilian
David R. Scott	U.S. Air Force
Clifton C. Williams, Jr.	U.S. Marine Corps

** *Were killed in airplane crashes.*

KNOWN RUSSIAN COSMONAUTS***

Valery S. Bykovsky	Air Force
Yuri A. Gagarin	Air Force
Andrian G. Nikolayev	Air Force
Pavel R. Popovich	Air Force
Valentina Tereshkova*	Civilian
Gherman S. Titov	Air Force
Konstantin Feoktistov	Air Force
Vladimir Komarov	Air Force
Boris Yegorov	Civilian
Aleksei A. Leonov	Air Force
Pavel I. Belyayev	Air Force

*female

***Space officials estimate many more in training

PRINCIPAL USES OF LAUNCH VEHICLES

Vehicle	*Employment*
Scout	Small Explorer satellites and geoprobes such as P-21 and P-21a.
Delta	Meteorological satellites (TIROS); Communications satellites (Telstar, Echo, Relay, and Syncom); and scientific satellites such as Explorers XII, XIV, XV, and XVII, Ariel, Orbiting Solar Observatory, and the Interplanetary Explorers.
Thor-Agena B	Scientific satellites such as Alouette, Orbiting Geophysical Observatory, applications satellites such as Advanced Echo communications satellite and Nimbus weather satellite.
Atlas D	Project Mercury.
Atlas-Agena B	Unmanned lunar and interplanetary probes such as Ranger Lunar Orbiter, and Mariner; Orbiting Astronomical Observatory; heavy advanced communications satellites; Project Gemini experiments.
Atlas-Centaur	Surveyor spacecraft for soft landing on the moon; advanced spacecraft of the Mariner type for exploration of Mars and Venus.

Titan II	Project Gemini.
Titan III	U.S. Air Force Manned Orbital Laboratory.
Saturn I	Project Apollo earth orbital flights of boilerplate command and service modules.
Saturn IB	Project Apollo earth orbital flights of manned command, service and lunar excursion modules (complete Apollo spacecraft); orbital rendezvous rehearsals.
Saturn V	Project Apollo lunar exploration missions.

APOLLO SPECIFICATION DATA

	Command Module	*Service Module*	*Lunar Excursion Module*
Shape:	Cone	Cylinder	Helicopter-like cab on legs
Height:	11.7 ft.	12.9 ft.	19 ft. (on legs)
Diameter:	12.8 ft. (base)	12.8 ft.	19 ft.
Take-off weight:	9,500 (approx.)	Less than 50,000	Less than 30,000; The adapter weighs approx. 3,500
Primary materials:	Aluminum alloy Stainless steel Titanium	Aluminum alloy Stainless steel Titanium	
Mission:	Crew quarters and control center for moon trip and return	Propulsion from moon and course correction. Houses support systems for command module	Land astronauts on moon and return them to the command module
Principal contractor	North American Aviation's Space and Information Systems Division	North American Aviation's Space and Information Systems Division	Grumman Aircraft Engineering

GLOSSARY OF FREQUENTLY USED SPACE TERMS

The following material has been excerpted from the Short Glossary of Space Terms, NASA publication SP–1.

ablating material. A material designed to dissipate heat by vaporizing or melting.
Ablating materials are used on the surfaces of some reentry vehicles. The heat is carried away from the surface by a loss of mass (liquid or vapor).

abort. To cancel or cut short a flight.

absolute zero. The theoretical temperature at which all molecular motion ceases.

acceleration. The rate of change of velocity.

accelerometer. An instrument which measures acceleration or gravitational forces capable of imparting acceleration.

active. Transmitting a signal, as "active satellite," in contrast to "passive."

adsorption. The adhesion of a thin film of liquid or gas to the surface of a solid substance.

aerodynamic heating. The heating of a body produced by passage of air or other gases over the body, significant chiefly at high speeds, caused by friction and by compression processes.

aerodynamics. The science that treats of the motion of air and other gaseous fluids, and of the forces acting on bodies when the bodies move through such fluids, or when such fluids move against or around the bodies, as "his research in aerodynamics."

aeroembolism. 1. The formation or liberation of gases in the blood vessels of the body, as brought on by a change from a high, or relatively high, atmospheric pressure to a lower one. 2. The disease or condition caused by the formation or liberation of gases in the body. The disease is characterized principally by neuralgic pains, cramps, and swelling, and sometimes results in death. Also called "decompression sickness."

aerospace. (From aeronautics and space.) Of or pertaining to both the earth's atmosphere and space, as in "aerospace industries."

aerospace medicine. That branch of medicine dealing with the effects of flight through the atmosphere or in space upon the human body, and with the prevention or cure of physiological or psychological malfunctions arising from these effects.

aerothermodynamic border. An altitude at about 100 miles, above which the atmosphere is so rarefied that the motion of an object through it at high speeds generates no significant surface heat.

analog computer. A computing machine that works on the principle of measuring, as distinguished from counting, in which the input data are made analogous to a measurement continuum, such as voltages, linear lengths, resistances, light intensities, etc., which can be manipulated by the computer.

angel. A radar echo caused by a physical phenomenon not discernible to the eye.

anoxia. A complete lack of oxygen available for physiological use within the body.

apogee. In an orbit about the earth, the point at which the satellite is farthest from the earth; the highest altitude reached by a sounding rocket.

apogee rocket. A rocket attached to a satellite or spacecraft designed to fire when the craft is at apogee, the point farthest from the earth in orbit. The effect of the apogee rocket is to establish a new orbit farther from the earth or to allow the craft to escape from earth orbit.

arc-jet engine. A type of electrical rocket engine in which the propellant gas is heated by passing through an electric arc.

artificial gravity. A simulated gravity established within a space vehicle, as by rotating a cabin about an axis of a spacecraft, the centrifugal force generated being similar to the force of gravity.

astro. A prefix meaning "star" or "stars" and, by extension, sometimes used as the equivalent of "celestial," as in astronautics.

astrobiology. The study of living organisms on celestial bodies other than the earth.

astronaut. 1. A person who occupies a space vehicle. 2. Specifically one of the test pilots selected to participate in Project Mercury, the first U.S. program for manned space flight.

astronautics. 1. The art, skill, or activity of operating space vehicles. 2. In a broader sense, the science of space flight.

atmosphere. The envelope of air surrounding the earth; also the body of gases surrounding or comprising any planet or other celestial body.

atomic clock. A precision clock that depends for its operation on an electrical oscillator (as a quartz crystal) regulated by the natural vibration frequencies of an atomic system (as a beam of cesium atoms or ammonia molecules).

attitude. The position or orientation of an aircraft, spacecraft, etc., either in motion or at rest, as determined by the relationship between its axes and some reference line or plane such as the horizon.

axis. (pl. axes) 1. A straight line about which a body rotates, or around which a plane figure may rotate to produce a solid; a line of symmetry. 2. One of a set of reference lines for certain systems of coordinates.

backup. 1. An item kept available to replace an item which fails to perform satsifactorily. 2. An item under development intended to perform the same general function performed by another item also under development.

ballistics. The science that deals with the motion, behavior, and effects of projectiles, especially bullets, aerial bombs, rockets, or the like; the science or art of designing and hurling projectiles so as to achieve a desired performance.

balloon-type rocket. A rocket, such as Atlas, that requires the pressure of its propellants (or other gases) within it to give it structural integrity.

beam. A ray or collection of focused rays of radiated energy. Radio waves used as a navigation aid.

beam-rider. A craft following a beam, particularly one which does so automatically, the beam providing the guidance.

bipropellant. A rocket propellant consisting of two unmixed or uncombined chemicals (fuel and oxidizer) fed to the combustion chamber separately.

bird. A colloquial term for a rocket, satellite, or spacecraft.

black box. Colloquially, any unit, usually an electronic device such as an amplifier, which can be mounted in a rocket, spacecraft, or the like as a single package.

blackout. 1. A fadeout of radio communications due to environmental factors such as ionospheric disturbances, or a plasma sheath surrounding a reentry vehicle. 2. A condition in which vision is temporarily obscured by a blackness, accompanied by a dullness of certain of the other senses, brought on by decreased blood pressure in the head and a consequent lack of oxygen, as may occur in pulling out of a high-speed dive in an airplane.

blockhouse. A structure, often built underground or partly underground, and sometimes dome-shaped, to provide protection against blast, heat, or explosion during rocket launchings or related activities; specifically, such a structure at a launch site that houses electronic control instruments used in launching a rocket.

boilerplate. As in "boilerplate capsule," a metal copy of the flight model, the structure or components of which are heavier than the flight model.

boiloff. The vaporization of a cold propellant such as liquid oxygen or liquid hydrogen, as the temperature of the propellant mass rises as in the tank of a rocket being readied for launch.

booster engine. An engine, especially a booster rocket, that adds its thrust to the thrust of the sustainer engine.

booster rocket. 1. A rocket engine, either solid or liquid fuel, that assists the normal propulsive system or sustainer engine of a rocket or aeronautical vehicle in some phase of its flight. 2. A rocket used to set a missile vehicle in motion before another engine takes over.

In sense 2 the term "launch vehicle" is more commonly used.

boostglide vehicle. A vehicle (half aircraft, half spacecraft) designed to fly to the limits of the sensible atmosphere, then be boosted by rockets into the space above, returning to earth by gliding under aerodynamic control.

breakoff phenomenon. The feeling which sometimes occurs during high-altitude flight of being totally separated and detached from the earth and human society. Also called the "breakaway phenomenon."

burn. A period during which a rocket engine is firing, as in "second burn," the second period during a flight in which the engine is firing.

burnout. 1. An act or instance of the end of fuel and oxidizer burning in a rocket; the time at which this burnout occurs. Compare **cutoff.** 2. An act or instance of something burning out or of overheating; specifically, an act or instance of a rocket combustion chamber, nozzle, or other part overheating so as to result in damage or destruction.

capsule. 1. A boxlike component or unit, often sealed. 2. A small, sealed, pressurized cabin with an internal environment which will support life in a man or animal during extremely high altitude flight, space flight, or emergency escape.

centrifuge. Specifically, a large motor-driven apparatus with a long arm at the end of which human and animal subjects or equipment can be revolved and rotated at various speeds to simulate very closely the prolonged accelerations encountered in high-performance aircraft, rockets, and spacecraft.

chase pilot. A pilot who flies in an escort airplane advising a pilot who is making a check, training, or research flight in another craft.

checkout. A sequence of actions taken to test or examine a launch vehicle or spacecraft as to its readiness to perform its intended function.

closed ecological system. A system that provides for the maintenance of life in an isolated living chamber such as a spacecraft cabin by means of a cycle wherein exhaled carbon dioxide, urine, and other waste matter are converted chemically or by photosynthesis into oxygen, water, and food.

command. A signal which initiates or triggers an action in the device which receives the signal.

communications satellite. A satellite designed to reflect or relay radio or other communications waves.

companion body. A nose cone, last-stage rocket, or other body that orbits along with an earth satellite.

complex. Entire area of launch site facilities. This includes blockhouse, launch pad, gantry, etc. Also referred to as a "launch complex."

computer. A machine for carrying out calculations and performing specified transformations on information.

configuration. A particular type of a specific aircraft, rocket, etc., which differs from others of the same model by virtue of the arrangement of its components or by the addition or omission of auxiliary equipment as "long-range configuration," "cargo configuration."

console. An array of controls and indicators for the monitoring and control of a particular sequence of actions, as in the checkout of a rocket, a countdown action, or a launch procedure.

A console is usually designed around desklike arrays. It permits the operator to monitor and control different activating instruments, data recording instruments, or event sequencers.

cosmic dust. Small meteoroids of a size similar to dust.

cosmic rays. The extremely high energy subatomic particles which bombard the atmosphere from outer space.

countdown. The time period in which a sequence of events is carried out to launch a rocket; the sequence of events.

cutoff. An act or instance of shutting something off; specifically in rocketry, an act or instance of shutting off the propellent flow in a rocket, or of stopping the combustion of the propellant.

deep space net. A combination of three radar and communications stations in the United States, Australia, and South Africa so located as to keep a spacecraft in deep space under observation at all times.

deep space probes. Spacecraft designed for exploring space to the vicinity of the moon and beyond. Deep space probes with specific missions may be referred to as "lunar probe," "Mars probe," "solar probe," etc.

destruct. The deliberate action of destroying a rocket vehicle after it has been launched, but before it has completed its course.

Destructs are executed when the rocket gets off its plotted course or functions in a way so as to become a hazard.

digital computer. A computer which operates on the principle of counting as opposed to measuring.

dish. A parabolic type of radio or radar antenna, roughly the shape of a soup bowl.

drogue parachute. A type of parachute attached to a body, used to slow it down; also called "deceleration parachute," or "drag parachute."

ecliptic. The apparent annual path of the sun among the stars

ecological system. A habitable environment, either created artificially, such as in a manned space vehicle, or occurring naturally, such as the environment on the surface of the earth, in which man, animals, or other organisms can live in mutual relationship with each other.

Ideally, the environment furnishes the sustenance for life, and the resulting waste products revert or cycle back into the environment to be used again for the continuous support of life.

ejection capsule. 1. In an aircraft or manned spacecraft, a detachable compartment serving as a cockpit or cabin, which may be rejected as a unit and parachuted to the ground. 2. In an artificial satellite, probe, or unmanned spacecraft, a boxlike unit usually containing recording instruments or records of observed data, which may be ejected and returned to earth by a parachute or other deceleration device.

electric propulsion. The generation of thrust for a rocket engine involving acceleration of a propellant by some electrical device such as an arc jet, ion engine, or magnetohydrodynamic accelerator.

electron. The subatomic particle that possesses the smallest possible electric charge.

electronic data processing. The use of electronic devices and systems in the processing of data so as to interpret the data and put it into usable form.

escape velocity. The speed which a particle or larger body must attain in order to escape from the gravitational field of a planet or star.

The escape velocity from Earth is approximately 7 miles per sec.

exosphere. The outermost, or topmost portion of the atmosphere.

explosive bolt. A bolt incorporating an explosive which can be detonated on command, thus destroying the bolt. Explosive bolts are used, for example, in separating a satellite from a rocket.

extraterrestrial. From outside the earth.

eyeballs in, eyeballs out. Terminology used by test pilots to describe the acceleration experienced by the person being accelerated. Thus the acceleration experienced by an astronaut at liftoff is "eyeballs in" positive g in terms of vehicle acceleration), and the acceleration experienced when retrorockets fire is "eyeballs out" (negative g in terms of vehicle acceleration).

fallaway section. A section of a rocket vehicle that is cast off and separates from the vehicle during flight, especially such a section that falls back to the earth.

fatigue. A weakening or deterioration of metal or other material, or of a member, occurring under load, especially under repeated, cyclic, or continued loading.

fixed satellite. An earth satellite that orbits from west to east at such a speed as to remain constantly over a given place on the earth's equator.

free fall. 1. The fall or drop of a body, such as a rocket, not guided, not under thrust, and not retarded by a parachute or other braking device. 2. Weightlessness.

g or G. An acceleration equal to the acceleration of gravity, approximately 32.2 feet per second per second at sea level; used as a unit of stress measurement for bodies undergoing acceleration.

gantry. A frame structure that spans over something, as an elevated platform that runs astride a work area, supported by wheels on each side; specifically, short for "gantry crane" or "gantry scaffold."

gantry scaffold. A massive scaffolding structure mounted on a bridge or platform supported by a pair of towers or trestles that normally run back and forth on parallel tracks, used to assemble and service a large rocket on its launching pad. Often shortened to "gantry." Also called "service tower."

garbage. Miscellaneous objects in orbit, usually material ejected or broken away from a launch vehicle or satellite.

gimbal. 1. A device with two mutually perpendicular and intersecting axes of rotation, thus giving free angular movement in two directions, on which an engine or other object may be mounted. 2. In a gyro, a support which provides the spin axis with a degree of freedom.

gravity. The force imparted by the earth to a mass on, or close to the earth.

g-suit or G-suit. A suit that exerts pressure on the abdomen and lower parts of the body to prevent or retard the collection of blood below the chest under positive acceleration.

g-tolerance. A tolerance in a person or other animal, or in a piece of equipment, to an acceleration of a particular value.

guidance. The process of directing the movements of an aeronautical vehicle or space vehicle, with particular reference to the selection of a flight path or trajectory.

heat exchanger. A device for transferring heat from one fluid to another without intermixing the fluids.

heat shield. Any device that protects something from heat.

heat sink. A material capable of absorbing heat; a device utilizing such a material and used as a thermal protection device on a spacecraft or reentry vehicle.

hold. During a countdown: To halt the sequence of events until an impediment has been removed so that the countdown can be resumed, as in "T minus 40 and holding."

hot test. A propulsion system test conducted by actually firing the propellants.

human engineering. The art or science of designing, building, or equipping mechanical devices or artificial environments to the anthropometric, physiological, or psychological requirements of the men who will use them.

hypersonic. 1. Pertaining to hypersonic flow. 2. Pertaining to speeds of Mach 5 or greater.

hypoxia. Oxygen deficiency in the blood, cells, or tissues of the body in such degree as to cause psychological and physiological disturbances.

igniter. Any device used to begin combustion, such as a spark plug in the combustion chamber of a jet engine, or a squib used to ignite fuel in a rocket.

impact area. The area in which a rocket strikes the earth's surface.

Used specifically in reference to the "impact area" of a rocket range.

impact bag. An inflatable bag attached to a spacecraft or reentry capsule to absorb part of the shock of landing.

insertion. The process of putting an artificial satellite into orbit. Also the time of such action.

ionosphere. The part of the earth's outer atmosphere where ions and electrons are present in quantities sufficient to affect the propagation of radio waves.

laser. (From light amplification by stimulated emission of radiation). A device for producing light by emission of energy stored in a molecular or atomic system when stimulated by an input signal.

launch pad. The load-bearing base or platform from which a rocket vehicle is launched.

launch ring. The metal ring on the launch pad on which a missile stands before launch.

launch vehicle. Any device which propels and guides a spacecraft into orbit about the earth or into a trajectory to another celestial body. Often called "booster."

launch window. An interval of time during which a rocket can be launched to accomplish a particular purpose as "liftoff occurred 5 minutes after the beginning of the 82-minute launch window."

liftoff. The action of a rocket vehicle as it separates from its launch pad in a vertical ascent.

A liftoff is applicable only to vertical ascent; a takeoff is applicable to ascent at any angle. A liftoff is action performed by a rocket; a launch is action performed upon a rocket or upon a satellite or spaceship carried by a rocket.

liquid-propellant rocket engine. A rocket engine fueled with a propellant or propellants in liquid form. Also called "liquid-propellant rocket."

longitudinal axis. The fore-and-aft line through the center of gravity of a craft.

lox. 1. Liquid oxygen. Used attributively as in "lox tank," "lox unit." Also called "loxygen." 2. To load the fuel tanks of a rocket vehicle with liquid oxygen. Hence, "loxing."

magnitude. Relative brightness of a celestial body. The smaller the magnitude number, the brighter the body.

main stage. 1. In a multistage rocket, the stage that develops the greatest amount of thrust, with or without booster engines. 2. In a single-stage rocket vehicle powered by one or more engines, the period when full thrust (at or above 90 percent) is attained. 3. A sustainer engine, considered as a stage after booster engines have fallen away, as in the main stage of the Atlas.

maser. An amplifier utilizing the principle of microwave amplification by stimulated emission of radiation. Emission of energy stored in a molecular or atomice system by a microwave power supply is stimulated by the input signal.

mass. The measure of the amount of matter in a body, thus its inertia.

The weight of a body is the force with which it is attracted by the earth.

mass ratio. The ratio of the mass of the propellant charge of a rocket to the total mass of the rocket charged with the propellant.

mate. To fit together two major components of a system.

memory. The component of a computer, control system, guidance system, instrumented satellite, or the like designed to provide ready access to data or instructions previously recorded so as to make them bear upon an immediate problem, such as the guidance of a physical object, or the analysis and reduction of data.

meteor. In particular, the light phenomenon which results from the entry into the earth's atmosphere of a solid particle from space: more generally, any physical object or phenomenon associated with such an event.

meteorological rocket. A rocket designed primarily for routine upper-air observation (as opposed to research) in the lower 250,000 feet of the atmosphere, especially that portion inaccessible to baloons; i.e., above 100,000 feet. Also called "rocketsonde."

mini. A contraction of "miniature" used in combination, as in "minicomponent," "miniradio," "minitransistor."

miniaturize. To construct a functioning miniature of a part or instrument. Said of telemetering instruments or parts used in an earth satellite or rocket vehicle, where room is at a premium. Hence "miniaturized," "miniaturization."

missile. Any object thrown, dropped, fired, launched, or otherwise projected with the purpose of striking a target. Short for "ballistic missile," "guided missile."

Missile is loosely used as a synonym for "rocket" or "spacecraft" by some careless writers.

mockup. A full-sized replica or dummy of something, such as a spacecraft, often made of some substitute material, such as wood and sometimes incorporating functioning pieces of equipment, such as engines.

module. 1. A self-contained unit of a launch vehicle or spacecraft which serves as a building block for the overall structure. The module is usually designated by its primary function as "command module," "lunar landing module," etc. 2. A one-package assembly of functionally associated electronic parts; usually a plug-in unit.

multistage rocket. A vehicle having two or more rocket units, each unit firing after the one in back of it has exhausted its propellant. Normally, each unit, or stage, is jettisoned after completing its firing. Also called a "multiple-stage rocket" or, infrequently, a "step rocket."

neutron. A subatomic particle with no electric charge, having a mass slightly more than the mass of the proton.

noise. Any undesired sound. By extension, noise is any unwanted disturbance within a useful frequency band, such as undesired electric waves in a transmission channel or device. When caused by natural electrical discharges in the atmosphere noise may be called "static."

nosecone. The cone-shaped leading end of a rocket vehicle, consisting of (a) of a chamber or chambers in which a satellite, instruments, animals, plants, or auxiliary equipment may be carried, and (b) of an outer surface built to withstand high temperatures generated by aerodynamic heating.

In a satellite vehicle, the nosecone may become the satellite itself after separating from the final stage of the rocket or it may be used to shield the satellite until orbital speed is accomplished, then separating from the satellite.

nozzle. Specifically, the part of a rocket thrust champer assembly in which the gases produced in the chamber are accelerated to high velocities.

orbit. 1. The path of a body or particle under the influence of a gravitational or other force. For instance, the orbit of a celestial body is its path relative to another body around which it revolves. 2. To go around the earth or other body in an orbit.

orbital period. The interval between successive passages of a satellite.

orbital velocity. 1. The average velocity at which an earth satellite or other orbiting body travels around its primary. 2. The velocity of such a body at any given point in its orbit, as in "its orbital velocity at the apogee is less than at the perigee."

oxidizer. Specifically, a substance (not necessarily containing oxygen) that supports the combustion of a fuel or propellant.

pad. The platform from which a rocket vehicle is launched. See "launch pad."

paraglider. A flexible-winged, kite-like vehicle designed for use in a recovery system for launch vehicles or as a reentry vehicle.

passive. Reflecting a signal without transmission, as "Echo is a passive satellite." Contrasted with "active."

payload. 1. Originally, the revenue-producing portion of an aircraft's load, e.g., passengers, cargo, mail, etc. 2. By extension, that which an aircraft, rocket, or the like carries over and above what is necessary for the operation of the vehicle during its flight.

perigee. That orbital point nearest the earth when the earth is the center of attraction.

That orbital point farthest from the earth is called "apogee." Perigee and apogee are used by many writers in referring to orbits of satellites, especially artificial satellites, around any planet or satellite, thus avoiding coinage of new terms for each planet and moon.

pickoff. A sensing device, used in combination with a gyroscope in an automatic pilot or other automatic or robot apparatus, that responds to angular movement to create a signal or to effect some type of control.

pickup. A device that converts a sound, view, or other form of intelligence into corresponding electric signals (e.g., a microphone, a television camera, or a phonograph pickup).

pip. Signal indication on the scope of an electronic instrument, produced by a short, sharply peaked pulse of voltage. Also called "blip."

pitchover. The programed turn from the vertical that a rocket under power takes as it describes an arc and points in a direction other than vertical.

posigrade rocket. An auxiliary rocket which fires in the direction in which the vehicle is pointed, used for example in separating two stages of a vehicle.

pressure suit. A garment designed to provide the human body an environment above ambient pressure so that respiratory and circulatory functions may continue normally, or nearly so, under low-pressure conditions, such as occur at high altitudes or in space without benefit of a pressurized cabin.

pressurized. Containing air, or other gas, at a pressure that is higher than the pressure outside the container.

prestage. A step in the action of igniting a large liquid rocket taken prior to the ignition of the full flow, and consisting of igniting a partial flow of propellants into the thrust chamber.

primary body. The spatial body about which a satellite or other body orbits, or from which it is escaping, or towards which it is falling.

The primary body of the moon is the earth; the primary body of the earth is the sun.

probe. Any device inserted in an environment for the purpose of obtaining information about the environment, specifically, an instrumented vehicle moving through the upper atmosphere or space, or landing upon another celestial body in order to obtain information about the specific environment.

proving stand. A test stand for reaction engines, especially rocket engines.

purge. To rid a line or tank of residual fluid, especially of fuel or oxygen in the tanks or lines of a rocket after a test firing or simulated test firing.

radiation shield. 1. A device used on certain types of instruments to prevent unwanted radiation from biasing the measurement of a quantity. 2. A device used to protect bodies from the harmful effects of nuclear radiation, cosmic radiation, or the like.

radio astronomy. The study of celestial objects through observation of radiofrequency waves emitted or reflected by these objects.

radio telescope. A device for receiving, amplifying, and measuring the intensity of radio waves originating outside the earth's attmosphere.

reaction control system. A system of controlling the attitude of a craft when outside the atmosphere by using jets of gas in lieu of aerodynamic control surfaces.

reaction engine. An engine that develops thrust by its reaction to ejection of a substance from it; specifically, such an engine that ejects a jet or stream of gases created by the burning of fuel within the engine.

readout. The action of a radio transmitter transmitting data either instantaneously with the acquisition of the data or by play of a magnetic tape upon which the data have been recorded.

readout station. A recording or receiving ratio station at which data are received from a transmitter in a probe, satellite, or other spacecraft.

real time. Time in which reporting on events or recording of events is simultaneous with the events.

recovery. The procedure or action that obtains when the whole of a satellite, or a section, instrumentation package, or other part of a rocket vehicle is recovered after a launch; the result of this procedure.

recycle. In a countdown: To stop the count and to return to an earlier point in the countdown, as in "we have recycled, now at T minus 80 and counting."

reentry. The event occurring when a spacecraft or other object comes back into the sensible atmosphere after being rocketed to altitudes above the sensible atmosphere; the action involved in this event.

reentry vehicle. A space vehicle designed to return with its payload to earth through the sensible atmosphere.

reentry window. The area at the limits of the earth's atmosphere through which a spacecraft in a given trajectory can pass to accomplish a successful reentry.

rendezvous. The event of two or more objects meeting at a preconceived time and place.

A rendezvous would be involved, for example, in servicing or resupplying a space station.

retrorocket. A rocket fitted on or in a spacecraft, satellite, or the like to produce thrust opposed to forward motion.

revolution. Motion of a celestial body in its orbit; circular motion about an axis usually external to the body.

rocket. A projectile, pyrotechnic device, or flying vehicle propelled by a rocket engine.

rocket engine. A reaction engine that contains within itself, or carries along with itself, all the substances necessary for its operation or for the consumption or combustion of its fuel, not requiring intake of any outside substance and hence capable of operation in outer space. Also called "rocket motor."

rocket propellant. Any agent used for consumption or combustion in a rocket and from which the rocket derives its thrust, such as a fuel, oxidizer, additive, catalyst, or any compound or mixture of these.

rocketsonde. Meterological rocket.

roll. The rotational or oscillatory movement of an aircraft or similar body which takes place about a longitudinal axis through the body—called "roll" for any amount of such rotation.

rotation. Turning of a body about an axis within the body, as the daily rotation of the earth.

rumble. A form of combustion instability, especially in a liquid-propellant rocket engine, characterized by a low-pitched, low-frequency rumbling noise.

satellite. 1. An attendant body that revolves about another body, the primary; especially in the solar system, a secondary body, or moon, that revolves about a planet. 2. A manmade object that revolves about a spatial body, such as Explorer I orbiting about the earth.

scrub. To cancel a scheduled rocket firing, either before or during countdown.

sensible atmosphere. That part of the atmosphere that offers resistance to a body passing through it.

sensor. The component of an instrument that converts an input signal into a quantity which is measured by another part of the instrument.

service tower = gantry scaffold.

shot. An act or instance of firing a rocket, especially from the earth's surface, as "the shot carried the rocket 200 miles."

sidereal. Of or pertaining to the stars.

solid propellant. Specifically, a rocket propellant in solid form, usually containing both fuel and oxidizer combined or mixed and formed into a monolithic (not powdered or granulated) grain.

solid-propellant rocket engine. A rocket engine using a solid propellant. Such engines consist essentially of a combustion chamber containing the propellant, and a nozzle for the exhaust jet, although they often contain other components, as grids, liners, etc. See **rocket engine.**

sonic. 1. Aerodynamics: Of or pertaining to the speed of sound; that moves at the speed of sound, as in 'sonic flow'; designed to operate or perform at the speed of sound, as in "sonic leading edge." 2. Of or pertaining to sound, as in "sonic amplifier."

sonic boom. A noise caused by the shock wave that emanates from an aircraft or other object traveling in the atmosphere at or above the speed of sound.

sonic speed. The speed of sound; by extension, the speed of a body traveling at Mach 1.

sophisticated. Complex and intricate; making use of advanced art; requiring special skills to operate.

sounding. 1. In geophysics, any penetration of the natural environment for scientific observation. 2. In meteorology, same as upper-air observation. However, a common connotation is that of a single complete radiosonde observation.

sounding rocket. A rocket designed to explore the atmosphere within 4,000 miles of the earth's surface.

space. 1. Specifically, the part of the universe lying outside the limits of the earth's atmosphere. 2. More generally, the volume in which all spatial bodies, including the earth, move.

space-air vehicle. A vehicle that may be operated either within or above the sensible atmosphere.

spacecraft. Devices, manned and unmanned, which are designed to be placed into an orbit about the earth or into a trajectory to another celestial body.

space medicine. A branch of aerospace medicine concerned specifically with the health of persons who make, or expect to make, flights into space beyond the sensible atmosphere.

space simulator. A device which simulates some condition or conditions existing in space and used for testing equipment, or in training programs.

spatial. Pertaining to space.

stage. A propulsion unit of a rocket, especially one unit of a multistage rocket, including its own fuel and tanks.

stage-and-a-half. A liquid-rocket propulsion unit of which only part falls away from the rocket vehicle during flight, as in the case of booster rockets falling away to leave the sustainer engine to consume remaining fuel.

stationary orbit. An orbit in which an equatorial satellite revolves about the primary at the same angular rate as the primary rotates on its axis. From the primary, the satellite thus appears to be stationary over a point on the primary.

supersonic. Pertaining to speeds greater than the speed of sound.

sustainer engine. An engine that maintains the velocity of a missile or rocket vehicle, once it has achieved its programed velocity through use of a booster engine.

synchronous satellite. An equatorial west-to-east satellite orbiting the earth at an altitude of 22,300 statute miles at which altitude it makes one revolution in 24 hours, synchronous with the earth's rotation.

telemetry. The science of measuring a quantity or quantities, transmitting the measured value to a distant station, and there interpreting, indicating, or recording the quantities measured.

terrestrial. Pertaining to the earth.

thermal. Pertaining to heat or temperature.

thrust. 1. The pushing force developed by an aircraft engine or a rocket engine. 2. Specifically, in rocketry, the product of propellant mass flow rate and exhaust velocity relative to the vehicle.

tracking. The process of following the movement of a satellite or rocket by radar, radio, and photographic observations.

trajectory. In general, the path traced by any body, as a rocket, moving as a result of externally applied forces.

Trajectory is loosely used to mean "flight path" or "orbit."

transfer orbit. In interplanetary travel an elliptical trajectory tangent to the orbits of both the departure planet and the target planet.

transponder. A combined receiver and transmitter whose function is to transmit signals automatically when triggered by an interrogating signal.

T-time. Any specific time, minus or plus, as referenced to "zero," or "launch" time, during a countdown sequence that is intended to result in the firing of a rocket propulsion unit that launches a rocket vehicle or missile.

ullage. The amount that a container, such as a fuel tank, lacks of being full.

umbilical cord. Any of the servicing electrical or fluid lines between the ground or a tower and an upright rocket missile or vehicle before the launch. Often shortened to "unbilical".

vehicle. Specifically, a structure, machine, or device, such as an aircraft or rocket, designed to carry a burden through air or space; more restrictively, a rocket craft.

This word has acquired its specific meaning owing to the need for a term to embrace all flying craft, including aircraft and rockets.

vernier engine. A rocket engine of small thrust used primarily to obtain a fine adjustment in the velocity and trajectory of a ballistic missile or space vehicle just after the thrust cutoff of the last propulsion engine, and used secondarily to add thrust to a booster or sustainer engine. Also called "vernier rocket".

weight. The force with which an earthbound body is attracted toward the earth.

weightlessness. 1. A condition in which no acceleration, whether of gravity or other force can be detected by an observer within the system in question. 2. A condition in which gravitational and other external forces acting on a body produce no stress, either internal or external, in the body.

Any object falling freely in a vacuum is weightless, thus an unaccelerated satellite orbiting the earth is "weightless" although gravity affects its orbit. Weightlessness can be produced within the atmosphere in aircraft flying a parabolic flight path.

yaw. 1. The lateral rotational or oscillatory movement of an aircraft, rocket, or the like about a transverse axis. 2. The amount of this movement; i.e., the angle of yaw.

zero g=**weightlessness.**

INDEX

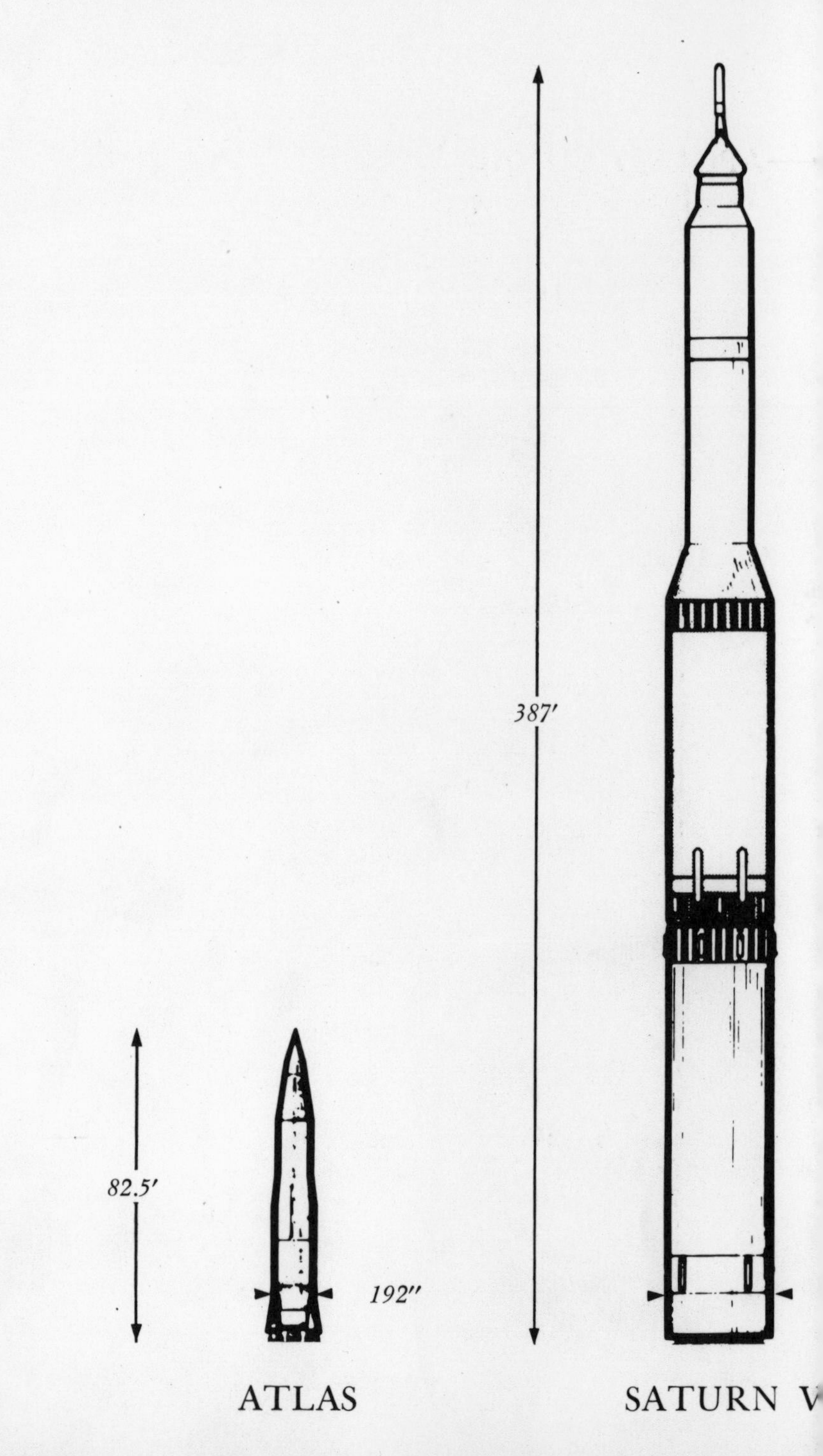
387′
82.5′
31′
192″
ATLAS
SATURN V

POLARIS